A Budding Book

First published in 1990 by Alan Sutton Publishing Limited,
an imprint of Sutton Publishing Limited
Phoenix Mill · Thrupp · Stroud · Gloucestershire

This edition first published in 1998 by Budding Books,
an imprint of Sutton Publishing Limited

A catalogue record for this book is available from the British Library

ISBN 1-84015-097-1

Typeset in Garamond 12/13.
Typesetting and origination by
Sutton Publishing Limited.
Printed in Great Britain by
WBC Ltd, Bridgend.

Doctor Syn's Christmas Mummers

RUSSELL THORNDIKE

Russell Thorndike (1885–1972) was born in Rochester. He had a close knowledge of the unique and eerie Romney Marsh area, known as the sixth continent and renowned for smuggling in the eighteenth and nineteenth centuries. From his researches into historical incidents connected with the celebrated Hawkhurst and Aldington gangs and anecdotes learnt from the patrons of the Ship Inn at Dymchurch about their smuggling ancestors, Russell Thorndike conceived the fictional Doctor Syn, the parson–smuggler known as the Scarecrow, whom he portrays as dominating the Marsh smuggling at the turn of the eighteenth century and during the nineteenth century.

Doctor Syn is the hero of seven Thorndike books, several films and a regular pageant at Dymchurch called the 'Day of Syn'. This story shows the mysterious Scarecrow appearing uninvited at the Christmas celebrations at Lympne Castle, a fine restored fourteenth-century manor house overlooking the Marsh.

· A Kent Christmas ·

In the days when Doctor Syn was Vicar of Dymchurch-under-the-Wall in the county of Kent, Yuletide was observed with the fullest ceremonial of ancient days.

Himself and Sir Antony Cobtree, the popular Squire and First Lord of the Level on Romney Marsh, had been students at Queen's College, Oxford, which has always maintained the Christmas ritual of the Boar's Head, so that it was not surprising to find in the hall of the Court House, the Squire's residence, that this delightful custom was carried out faithfully with the half-Latin, half-English carol, sung with due solemnity to the enjoyment of all the Squire's guests at Christmas dinner.

Both Squire and Vicar loved such curious whimsicalities, and perhaps the church choir who sang the carol, headed by Doctor Syn himself in the part of the Cantor with a cook's cap upon his reverend head, and the great dish held by the Squire's servants above him at their arms-length, was only eclipsed by the entertainment that followed on Christmas night. This was a play given by the local talent of the parish, and performed such as the old mummers had enacted it for generations upon other floors for stages than those on Romney Marsh. Doctor Syn, with a great love of drama, made a point of coaching the parishioners himself. They had enacted under his direction many old forms of Christmas Revels, but on the particular year when Captain Blain was guest at the Vicarage, and his men were quartered for the festival in the Tythe Barn, the good Doctor was determined to give his audience a more original entertainment that would in a spirit of Christmas fun hold out the finger of scorn at all the failings and failures of the year. The rehearsals had been carried out with the utmost secrecy, and all actors had been put under vow not to divulge anything of the matter to those not in the cast.

Now although the chief performance of the Dymchurch Mummers was the one presented at the Court House on

Christmas evening, there were others held on other nights by the same players in other great houses. Indeed, all the Lords of the Level extended Yuletide hospitality to their tenants, rich and poor, and the dates of such festivities were fixed by the various hosts for the convenience of Doctor Syn's Mummers who came to form the chief item of entertainment.

At every manor where these players were asked to perform, there was more than enough food and drink for any who cared to attend, and those who could walk or ride followed the Mummers wherever they went in order to partake in yet another feast.

Next in importance to the Dymchurch performance (which was ever the most popular because Sir Antony Cobtree was the host) was that given at Lympne Castle by Sir Henry Pembury upon the following night.

The castle hall was thronged not only by the tenants of the hills of Lympne and Aldington, but by everyone who could climb the inland cliff from the Lower Levels of the Marshes. Three districts these Marshes: Romney, Welland and Denge.

Sir Henry, Lord of Lympne, not only threw his castle doors open to all the common folk who cared to come, but took the occasion of this Boxing Night revel to send invitations to all the immediate gentry, most of whom joined in the dancing that followed the play.

One and all gladly accepted with thanks except Captain Blain, who curtly replied that he and his men would have witnessed the play the night previously at the Dymchurch Court House, and that he could not so far play into the Scarecrow's hands as to leave the Marsh when no doubt all good citizens would have left it for Lympne Castle. 'It is a great night for a "run", and no doubt the Scarecrow would have been delighted to think that I could leave my post and the road clear for him.'

. . . On entering the library of the castle, Doctor Syn at

'The Scarecrow' – alias Doctor Syn – in the Day of Syn celebrations at Dymchurch, 1989

once perceived that the Squire was in one of his worst tempers.

'Another letter from the Scarecrow?' asked Doctor Syn.

'Aye, Parson, and worse than the last one I received from him, as you will agree when you hear it, which you shall.'

'Let me see; the last one you had from him,' said the vicar, 'was a reproof that you had not invited him to the hunt with the Prince of Wales, and stating that he intended to come, which he did, and much to the Prince's amusement. That was bad enough, so please let me know what can be worse.'

'He now invites himself into my house,' replied the Squire. 'Aye, he intends to visit Lympne Castle without an invitation. Before it was at least out of doors. This time it will be within doors. Think of my unmarried daughters. The danger is frightful.'

With an effort Doctor Syn repressed the smile which he felt inwardly at the thought of the Scarecrow having designs upon anything so unattractive as the Squire's unwieldy daughters. Aloud he said: 'I think you may dismiss any fear of harm in that direction. Your young ladies have too many gallant followers, I should hope. So many who would protect them with their lives.'

'Precious little good that would be,' snorted the Squire. 'None knows better than we that the Scarecrow does what he says he will and diddles everyone. Here, read the letter for yourself, and tell me what to do.'

Doctor adjusted his spectacles and smoothed out the paper which the Squire had crumpled in his rage. It was written in the usual scrawl that never had failed to disturb its receiver. A rough sketch of a scarecrow was the signature. The Doctor read it aloud:

> We are informed that as Lord of Lympne Castle you have asked rich and poor alike to your Christmas junketing. Thanks to the poor attempts to put down the contraband traffic by all concerned, we count ourselves amongst the rich of this district. We therefore have been expecting to hear from you. Unless you wish us to attend in the wrong spirit, you had best nail an invitation to us upon the Lympne Hill signpost. When hunting with the Prince of Wales I did not have the honour of meeting your beautiful daughters, a pleasure I am looking forward to. It will also be a pleasure to drink a toast beneath the rafters of your historic home.

'And what do you think of that?' gasped the Squire, as though he had only just learned the contents which he knew by heart.

'I think that Captain Blain will now certainly accept your invitation,' replied the doctor. 'His men will give confidence to us all by their presence, and he'll sit through the play twice without boredom if he thinks he has a chance of getting his prey.'

'You think the Scarecrow will come, as he says?' asked the Squire.

The doctor laughed and shook his head. 'No, sir. I think the whole thing is a decoy to get the King's men to the junketing, as he calls it, in order that he may have a free hand upon the Marsh. But I advise you not to let Captain Blain think that, for then he will not attend, and in case of accidents it will be as well to have your guests protected from the scoundrel. Though come to think of it, sir, the rascally Scarecrow is too wise to prepare such a trap for himself and then walk boldly into it.'

'Yes, yes, but that's all very well,' said the Squire testily. 'Just the thing he'd enjoy. Prepare a trap, as you say, and walk into it, and then have the laugh on us all by walking out of it again.'

'I think you will find that I am right this time,' replied the doctor. 'Our play will go through without any disaster, because the Scarecrow will be busy shifting kegs of brandy on the beach . . . .'

After many weeks of being baffled by the Scarecrow's wits, Captain Blain would not agree with Doctor Syn that the letter to Lympne was an idle piece of boasting. He pointed out that the rascal's threats had always been carried out, and he had every reason to think that this would be no exception, and he accepted the invitation to the castle on that ground.

During the days before Christmas, the Captain saw but little of his host, who was busy every evening training his

Mummers in their parts behind the closed doors of the school house. Also, the thick snow and severe wintry winds blowing across the bleak Marsh necessitated the Doctor walking on his parochial visits, which meant that his hours were fully occupied. But, for all that Doctor Syn, was more than ever cheerful, and could be seen striding along chuckling to himself as he went, over the merry quips and satirical jokes that were going to be good-humouredly pronounced by his characters. Never before had the village play gone so well, or been more enthusiastically praised by the critical ones as on that first performance at the Court House.

Even the victims of the many jokes laughed uproariously at their own expense. But it was the final scene that caused the sensation. When Beelzebub entered shouting, 'Here come I, old Beelzebub, and in my hand I carries my club,' he was rigged out in rags similar to those worn by the Scarecrow. And when he claimed the hand of the fairest lady in the room, and led her away to the gates of hell, St George, throwing off his white battle-cloak, was seen to be dressed as an Excise officer. It was all voted grand foolery, though Mipps pointed out many an able-bodied parishioner who seemed to be fearful at laughing too much at the vicar's attack upon the dread Scarecrow . . . .'

The castle hall was packed. In the front sat Sir Henry Pembury, keeping an anxious eye upon his daughters, the eldest of whom was sitting next to Captain Blain, and obviously very piqued at his lack of interest in her.

At the best of times the Captain was no man for the ladies, but the sight of Miss Fan, whom her detractors nicknamed the Dragoon, embarrassed him confoundedly, especially when she patted him playfully upon the sleeve whenever a flattering allusion was spoken about the King's good men. Blain was having no truck with such a she-dragon. Unfortunately for the lady the other seat next to her was reserved for Doctor Syn, who, as the author, kept leaving it vacant in order to retire behind the great screens that backed the stage. But the last scene cheered her up. On the entrance of Beelzebub, attended by two Night-riders, she giggled hysterically, especially when the masked devils brought in a keg of brandy with No Duty chalked upon it, and made the Squire of Lympne take a glass with them.

'And who's the brave man acting the Scarecrow, miss?' asked Blain.

'I recognize his voice in spite of his disguise,' she whispered loudly. 'It is the eldest Upton boy from Dymchurch. Very well-looking too. It is a pity he is masked so hideously. They are a very worthy family, as no doubt you know.'

'The Scarecrow won't approve of him,' growled the Captain. 'He'll be needing my protection I fancy.'

When this actor came to the front row and chose her as the fairest in the room, her delight and coyness knew no bounds. Everyone knew that this was but a compliment to their host, but Miss Fan took it as a compliment to her beauty. She accepted his hand and to the applause of the audience walked with him to the back of the stage so that the Lord from Darkness could salute her under the mistletoe. On their disappearance St George came forward to make his heroic speech, and was applauded for some minutes when he threw off his cloak and declared himself a true King's man. He then had to follow the devil into hell and drive him back, having rescued the fair maiden. He disappeared amongst much applause, but did not reappear for some minutes, and the audience could hear the actors behind the screens whispering and asking for Doctor Syn.

After some minutes of an embarrassed wait the officious Mipps popped behind the screens to investigate. After another wait he reappeared, craving the audience's indulgence.

'The fact is, my lords, ladies and gentlemen,' he said

'In comes I Beelzebub . . .'

solemnly, 'our principal actor appears to have disappeared. What's more, he seems to have took off Miss Pembury with him. Also, we can't see no trace of Doctor Syn, who was a-waiting to step forward at the conclusion of his play to accept your kind applause. He's gone, too. Perhaps he's achaperoning Miss Pembury, for the back door is open on to the terrace.

Suddenly Captain Blain sprang to his feet. 'Mr Mipps,' he cried out, 'who was acting the part of the Devil?'

'We ain't supposed to tell,' replied Mipps, 'but if you must know it was of them Uptons. Good, too.'

'Was it?' replied the Captain. 'Aye and he may be "was" unless we're quick. Sir Henry Pembury, I believe the Scarecrow had kept his word. I believe he has carried off your daughter under our noses. Quick, men. Fall in and follow me.'

There followed a general stampede of those brave enough to venture out of the door to the terrace. The King's men with drawn cutlasses pushed their way out, and the first sight that met their eyes was a dishevelled Miss Fan lying in the snow on the terrace steps.

Captain Blain seized hold of her and gave her a rough shaking as he shouted, 'Where did he go?'

Miss Fan pointed to a great tree at the foot of the terrace and then uttering a scream, fainted.

Leaving his heavy burden to be taken care of by others who were thronging out on to the terrace, the Captain, followed by his men, ran down the steps, and stumbled through the thick snow to the tree in question, where they found Doctor Syn and the eldest young Upton lashed to the trunk with coils of rope.

And away down the hill towards the Marsh they saw the hoof-marks of a horse.

Before the old Doctor could recover his speech, young Upton explained.

'We've been here for some minutes. We were seized, the Doctor and me, and dragged out here. It was Night-riders because we saw the great black horse, standing with three others which another Night-rider held. Presently out comes the Scarecrow with Miss Pembury in his arms. He seemed to be disentangling himself from her arms which were clutched round his neck. He finally got free of her and laid her in the snow, and then they all mounted and rode off single file down towards the Marsh.'

When Doctor Syn recovered later in the castle, he smiled at Sir Henry and said: 'You were right, sir. I was punished for making fun of the Scarecrow. What I cannot make out though is how did the rascal play his part so well according to you.'

'Most likely he watched it last night in the Dymchurch Court House,' suggested the Captain. 'He was, in my opinion, a better actor than poor young Upton.'

The next day Doctor Syn went out through the snow to visit a dying woman. On the way back, however, unknown to anyone, he visited Jimmie Bone, the Highwayman, in the Scarecrow's hidden stable.

'I hear, my good friend,' laughed the Doctor, 'that your performance was magnificent. I hope you enjoyed it as much as the audience?'

'My very revered Scarecrow,' replied the Highwayman, 'had I known all, I fear I should not have obeyed you. That Pembury woman, when I told her that I was the Scarecrow in truth, clung to me tighter than ever. I can feel her heart beating against me now. I always had an eye for a pretty wench, but oh, that woman!'

'Avoid all such conceit,' reproved the Parson. 'No doubt she clung to you in order to get the thousand guineas on the Scarecrow's head. You must not misinterpret her motive.'

'Well, I'll never hold up old Pembury's coach again, in case she embraces me again,' laughed the Highwayman.

Christmas Past on the North Downs

KEN THOMPSON

Ken Thompson worked at Little Betsoms Farm near Westerham between the wars as a boy and in 1950 took over the farm tenancy from his father. Little Betsoms was principally a sheep farm on the North Downs though some dairy cattle were kept and hay grown. This is his account of his boyhood Christmases on the north Kentish chalklands and of his father who was a handbell-ringer.

From Westerham you climb up to the North Downs and at the summit the land levels out. If you look to your left there's a pair of old slate cottages known as the Fort Cottages. The Fort Cottages were service cottages to the old Napoleonic fort behind, then pretty derelict and overgrown, and my father was employed as caretaker and gardener to the lodge at Westerham Heights. It was in number one Fort Cottages that I was born seventy-one years ago and when I look back over the years I recall that my first childhood memories were in that cottage.

It was 1923 and the approach to Christmas and I was wakened by the sound of ringing bells. I climbed out of my cot and opened the door into the living room where, to my amazement, I saw a number of whiskery men standing all round the room. The fire was flowing and it reflected their ruddy tanned faces and brass bells shining in their hands.

'You should be in bed,' said my mother.

But she was very good and let me stay and watch the bell-ringers. I can see them all now, their old faces shining. They'd obviously had a drink and were enjoying themselves. The oldest men seemed to have one bell in each hand, the others, two bells in each hand and then there was my father. I can remember even now the pride with which in later days he used to say, 'I had to play four in each hand.' When they turned their wrists the Christmas tunes rang out.

The bell-ringers visited each other's houses in turn and also went round to the big halls and houses. The object of this was to raise money for their societies and of course they'd get a drink. That's how it went on then. I was hardly more than three or four at that time. It's amazing how clear the memories are.

Ken Thompson and his father ploughing on the North Downs

'We kept sheep up on the North Downs . . .'

I remember too that my mother always kept a pig which was killed just before Christmas. Some of it was sold and some of it kept for the family.

Fort Cottages were at the end of an old lane that ran back maybe three-quarters of a mile off the road and at the end of that lane was Little Betsoms Farm, about ninety-five acres plus woodland. When I was five or six I was to move there with my parents when my father took over as tenant farmer. That takes me back to another childhood memory. It was Christmastime 1926 and when we all woke up on Christmas morning there was more snow than I think anyone had ever seen in their lifetime. Of course we kept sheep up on the North Downs – Romney Marsh sheep that came up from the marsh for the winter to get away from the wets – and by Boxing Day all those sheep had been drifted in. Well, there was my Uncle

Ken Thompson

Thew who was a gun-layer in the Navy, home for Christmas, and my brother Bill and my Father and they were all big chaps and out they went with their big coats on and their shovels and spades to see what they could do about finding the sheep. And about half past twelve in they came and they'd got all the sheep out. They'd dug about but the only way they could find the sheep was by spotting the numbers of little holes in the snow drifts made by the breathing of the sheep. When they'd found these air-holes they'd found the sheep. And they got them all home in the barn and put them in and made them comfortable and of course when these chaps came indoors they were more than pleased to have a drop of whisky and my mother was standing on the step waiting and so was I and they told us how they got out the sheep and they were really quite proud of what they'd done.

Now that snow went on and it got worse and it meant that farms like ours, high up on the North Downs, became isolated and food had to be dropped by bi-plane. I remember now walking with my brother to Westerham and walking right over the frozen drifts and over the hedges! You couldn't tell where the hedges were – the only things sticking out of the snow were tall trees and the tops of buildings. Of course the old church steeple in Westerham stood out like a landmark. And all the local men were out digging foot roads for none of the builders or anybody else for that matter could go to their work. It was a long time before the roads were clear but when they were I remember having to walk the two and a half miles to the bakers in Biggin Hill with a sledge and picking up six loaves at a time (great big double loaves) and dragging them back home. And that's another childhood memory.

Of course my mother used to talk to me about Christmas past but there wasn't much to tell because she came from a family of eighteen and their Christmases were pretty poverty stricken. She used to tell me that the only way they got any

Christmas at all was by going out carol singing at the big houses in Tatsfield. They'd do a bit of singing and they used to come up with a few halfpence and that would be taken home to her mother (my grandmother) and then they were alright for a bit of Christmas pudding. My mother told me that it was just a white pudding with a few currants so it wasn't the great big brown luscious affair that we have today.

There was a song she used to sing at Christmas about a sweetheart that got trapped in a chest and died, and I remember her now singing:

> The holly bough hung in the old oak hall,
> They searched all that night
> And they searched the next day . . . .

It was very moving.

The Mistletoe Bough

This was a very popular Christmas ballad in the nineteenth and early twentieth centuries in all the southern counties and is found extensively in the oral tradition. As well as the version Ken Thompson heard from his mother, another Kent folk singer, Les Waghorn, remembers it being sung in the Headcorn area between the wars. The

'The baron's retainers were blithe and gay'

Copper family of Rottingdean have a Sussex version and it is mentioned by Thomas Hardy in his novel A Loadicean *(1881).*

These versions probably derive from the ballad of the same name composed by Thomas Bayly (1797–1839), set to music by Sir Henry Bishop. The original heroine of the tale is Ginevra of the Orsini family of Modena, who hid herself in a chest during a game on her wedding night, but in the folk-song this event has merged with English traditions concerning the Lovell family.

The mistletoe hung from the Castle wall
The holly bough hung in the old oak hall

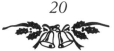

CHRISTMAS PEACE
AND CHRISTMAS
PLEASURE
BE WITH YOU IN
BOUNDLESS
MEASURE.
Victorian Christmas card

And the Baron's retainers were blithe and gay
All keeping their Christmas holiday.
The Baron beheld with a father's pride
His beautiful child, young Lovell's bride,
Whilst she with her bright eyes seemed to be
the star of that goodly company,

O the mistletoe bough
O the mistletoe bough

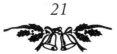

'I'm tired of dancing my love', she cried,
'Here tarry a moment for me to hide.
And Lovell, be sure thou art first to trace
The clue to my secret hiding place.'
Away she ran and her friends began
Each tower to search and each vault to scan
And young Lovell cried 'O where dost thou hide.
I long to find you my own dear bride.'

They searched all that night and they searched the next day,
They sought her in vain till a week passed away.
In the highest, the lowest, the loneliest spot,
Young Lovell sought wildly and found her not.
And years flew by and their grief at last
Was told as a sorrowing tale of the past
And when Lovell appeared, the children cried,
'See the old man weeps for his own dear bride.'

One day an old chest that had long lain hid
Was found in the castle, they raised the lid.
And a skeleton form lay mouldering there
In the bridal wreath of a lady fair.
O sad was her fate, in a yuletide jest,
She hid from her lord in the old oak chest.
It closed with a spring – what a dreadful doom
The bride lay clasped in a living tomb.

from

Pickwick Papers – 'Mr Wardle's Christmas Party'

CHARLES DICKENS

'I have many happy recollections connected with Kent, and am scarcely less interested in it than if I had been a Kentish man bred and born and had resided in the county all my life.'

In 1816, when Charles Dickens was four, his charming but irresponsible father moved with his family from Portsmouth to work in the Navy Pay Office in Chatham. For five years the family lived in a pleasant house in Ordnance Terrace, whose hilltop position overlooking a hayfield commanded a fine view over the River Medway. Two further years were spent in a more modest house in St Mary's Place, Chatham. These seven years in Kent were the happiest of Dickens' life and his impressions and memories of the Kentish towns and countryside never left him, reappearing continually in his novels. Dickens' honeymoon was spent in the little Kentish village of Chalk and it was here that he wrote some of the early chapters of Pickwick Papers. *At the height of his fame, Dickens left London for Kent, initially taking up residence in Broadstairs in the Fort (later renamed Bleak House), 'which stood prominently at the top of a breezy hill . . . with a cornfield between it and the sea.' Here he wrote the greatest part of* David Copperfield *and* Bleak House. *Perhaps his favourite Kentish home was Gadshill Place near Rochester where he lived from 1856 to his death in 1870 and where* Great Expectations *and* The Mystery of Edwin Drood *were written. The purchase of Gadshill was a dream realized. As a small boy, accompanying his father on a long walk in the countryside around Rochester they had come across this imposing dwelling and Dickens senior had suggested that if his son were to work very hard, one day he might very well own such a house.*

Pickwick Papers *was published in 1836 when Dickens was only twenty-five. The action soon moves from the London setting into that of Dickens' beloved Kent. The memorable Christmas at Dingley Dell and Mr Wardle's unstinting hospitality lovingly creates an early nineteenth-century house party at the most festive of seasons. Sandling near Maidstone is the probable location of Dingley Dell and Cob Tree Hall (now destroyed) is thought to have been the inspiration for Manor Farm, home of Mr Wardle and his extended family where the Pickwickians spent Christmas.*

The best sitting room at Manor Farm was a good, long, dark-panelled room with a high chimney-piece, and a capacious chimney, up which you could have driven one of the new patent cabs, wheels and all. At the upper end of the room, seated in a shady bower of holly and evergreens, were the two best fiddlers, and the only harp, in all Muggleton. In all sorts of recesses, and on all kinds of brackets, stood massive old silver candlesticks with four branches each. The carpet was up, the candles burnt bright, the fire blazed and crackled on the hearth, and merry voices and light-hearted laughter rang through the room. If any of the old English yeomen had turned into fairies when they died, it was just the place in which they would have held their revels.

If anything could have added to the interest of this agreeable scene, it would have been the remarkable fact of Mr Pickwick's appearing without his gaiters, for the first time within the memory of his oldest friends.

'You mean to dance?' said Wardle.

'Of course I do,' replied Mr Pickwick. 'Don't you see I am dressed for the purpose?' Mr Pickwick called attention to his speckled silk stockings, and smartly-tied pumps.

'*You* in silk stockings!' exclaimed Mr Tupman jocosely.

'And why not, sir – why not?' said Mr Pickwick, turning warmly upon him.

'Oh, of course there is no reason why you shouldn't wear them,' responded Mr Tupman.

'I imagine not, sir, I imagine not,' said Mr Pickwick in a very peremptory tone.

Mr Tupman had contemplated a laugh, but he found it was a serious matter; so he looked grave, and said they were a pretty pattern.

'I hope they are,' said Mr Pickwick, fixing his eyes upon his friend. 'You see nothing extraordinary in the stockings, *as* stockings, I trust, sir?'

'Certainly not. Oh, certainly not.' replied Mr Tupman. He walked away; and Mr Pickwick's countenance resumed its customary benign expression.

'We are all ready, I believe,' said Mr Pickwick, who was stationed with the old lady at the top of dance, and had already made four false starts, in his excessive anxiety to commence.

Christmas Eve at Mr Wardle's

'Then begin at once,' said Wardle. 'Now!'

Up struck the two fiddles and the one harp, and off went Mr Pickwick into hands across, when there was a general clapping of hands, and a cry of 'Stop, stop!'

'What's the matter!' said Mr Pickwick, who was only brought to by the fiddles and harp desisting, and could have been stopped by no other earthly power, if the house had been on fire.

'Where's Arabella Allen?' cried a dozen voices.

'And Winkle?' added Mr Tupman.

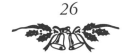

'Here we are!' exclaimed that gentleman, emerging with his pretty companion from the corner; as he did so, it would have been hard to tell which was the redder in the face, he or the young lady with the black eyes.

'What an extraordinary thing it is, Winkle,' said Mr Pickwick, rather pettishly, 'that you couldn't have taken your place before.'

'Not at all extraordinary,' said Mr Winkle.

'Well,' said Mr Pickwick, with a very expressive smile, as his eyes rested on Arabella, 'well, I don't know that it *was* extraordinary either, after all,'

However, there was no time to think more about the matter, for the fiddles and harp began in real earnest. Away went Mr Pickwick – hands across – down the middle to the very end of the room, and half-way up the chimney, back again to the door – poussette everywhere – loud stamp on the ground – ready for the next couple off again – all the figure over once more – another stamp to beat out the time – next couple, and the next, and the next again – never was such going! At last, after they had reached the bottom of the dance, and full fourteen couple after the old lady had retired in an exhausted state, and the clergyman's wife had been substituted in her stead, did that gentleman, when there was no demand whatever on his exertions, keep perpetually dancing in his place, to keep time to the music: smiling on his partner all the while with a blandness of demeanour which baffles all description . . . .

They all repaired to the large kitchen, in which the family were by this time assembled, according to annual custom on Christmas Eve, observed by old Wardle's forefathers from time immemorial.

From the centre of the ceiling of this kitchen, old Wardle had just suspended with his own hands, a huge branch of mistletoe, and this same branch of mistletoe instantaneously gave rise to a scene of general and delightful struggling and confusion; in the midst of which, Mr Pickwick, with a gallantry that would have done honour to a descendant of Lady Tollimglower herself, took the old lady by the hand, led her beneath the mystic branch, and saluted her in all courtesy and decorum. The old lady submitted to this piece of practical politeness with all the dignity which befitted so important and serious a solemnity, but the younger ladies, not being so thoroughly imbued with a superstitious veneration for the custom; or imagining that the value of a salute is very much enhanced if it cost a little trouble to obtain it, screamed and struggled, and ran into corners, and threatened and remonstrated, and did everything but leave the room, until some of the less adventurous gentlemen were on the point of desisting, when they all at once found it useless to resist any longer, and submitted to be kissed with a good grace. Mr Winkle kissed the young lady with the black eyes, and Mr Snodgrass kissed Emily, and Mr Weller, not being particular about the form of being under the mistletoe, kissed Emma and the other female servants, just as he caught them. As to the poor relations, they kissed everybody, not even excepting the plainer portions of the young lady visitors, who, in their excessive confusion, ran right under the mistletoe, as soon as it was hung up, without knowing it! Wardle stood with his back to the fire, surveying the whole scene, with the utmost satisfaction; and the fat boy took the opportunity of appropriating to his own use, and summarily devouring, a particularly fine mince-pie, that had been carefully put by for somebody else.

Now, the screaming had subsided, and faces were in a glow, and curls in a tangle, and Mr Pickwick, after kissing the old lady as before mentioned, was standing under the mistletoe, looking with a very pleased countenance on all that was passing around him, when the young lady with the black eyes, after a little whispering with the other young ladies, made a

Mr Pickwick plays Blind Man's Bluff

sudden dart forward, and, putting her arm round Mr Pickwick's neck, saluted him affectionately on the left cheek; and before Mr Pickwick distinctly knew what was the matter, he was surrounded by the whole body, and kissed by every one of them.

It was a pleasant thing to see Mr Pickwick in the centre of the group, now pulled this way, and then that, and first kissed on the chin, and then on the nose, and then on the spectacles: and to hear the peals of laughter which were raised on every side; but it was a still more pleasant thing to see Mr Pickwick, blinded shortly afterwards with a silk handkerchief, falling up against the wall, and scrambling into corners, and going through all the mysteries of blind-man's buff, with the utmost relish for the game, until at last he caught one of the poor relations, and then had to evade the blind-man himself, which he did with a nimbleness and agility that elicited the admiration and applause of all beholders. The poor relations caught the people who they thought would like it, and, when the game flagged, got caught themselves. When they were all tired of blind-man's buff, there was a great game at snap-dragon, and when fingers enough were burned with that, and all the raisins were gone, they sat down by the huge fire of blazing logs to a substantial supper, and a mighty bowl of wassail, something smaller than an ordinary wash-house copper, in which the hot apples were hissing and bubbling with a rich look, and a jolly sound, that were perfectly irresistible.

'This,' said Mr Pickwick, looking round him, 'this is, indeed, comfort.'

'Our invariable custom,' replied Mr Wardle. 'Everybody sits down with us on Christmas Eve, as you see them now – servants and all; and here we wait, until the clock strikes twelve, to usher Christmas in, and beguile the time with forfeits and old stories. Trundle, my boy, rake up the fire.'

Up flew the bright sparks in myriads as the logs were stirred. The deep red blaze sent forth a rich glow, that penetrated into the furthest corner of the room, and cast its cheerful tint on every face.

'Come,' said Wardle, 'a song – a Christmas song! I'll give you one, in default of a better.'

'Bravo!' said Mr Pickwick.

'Fill up,' cried Wardle. 'It will be two hours, good, before you see the bottom of the bowl through the deep rich colour of the wassail: fill up all round, and now for the song.'

Thus saying, the merry old gentleman, in a good, round, sturdy voice, commenced without more ado:

A CHRISTMAS CAROL

But my song I troll out, for CHRISTMAS stout,
The hearty, the true, and the bold;
A bumper I drain, and with might and main
Give three cheers for this Christmas old!
We'll usher him in with a merry din
That shall gladden his joyous heart,
And we'll keep him up, while there's bite or sup,
And in fellowship good, we'll part.

In his fine honest pride, he scorns to hide,
One jot of his hard-weather scars;
They're no disgrace, for there's much the same trace
On the cheeks of our bravest tars.
Then again I sing 'till the roof doth ring,
And it echoes from wall to wall—
To the stout old wight, fair welcome to-night,
As the King of the Seasons all!

This song was tumultuously applauded – for friends and dependants made a capital audience – and the poor relations, especially, were in perfect ecstacies of rapture. Again was the fire replenished, and again went the wassail round.

'How it snows!' said one of the men, in a low tone.

from

Shipwrecks of the Goodwins – 'A New Year's Wreck'

RICHARD LARN

'. . . The Goodwins I think they call the place, a very dangerous flat, and fatal, where the carcasses of many a tall ship lie buried, as they say.'

(Shakespeare, The Merchant of Venice*)*

The notorious Goodwin Sands (the 'ship-swallower'), lie parallel to the coast between Ramsgate and Deal, about four miles out to sea. They are about ten miles long and two miles wide and the stretch of water between them and the coast is called the 'Downs'. In good weather, the Goodwins become firm enough for landings and even cricket matches, but when the sea level rises they become soft and have entrapped scores of ships over the years.

The Goodwins are named after Earl Godwin, the father of King Harold, who traditionally owned them along with substantial parts of Kent. During stormy weather, when ships were in danger of running aground on the Sands, the Deal fishermen used to say that Earl Godwin and his court were hungry.

Richard Larn has written a most interesting book on the shipwrecks of the Goodwins and this extract deals with the wreck of the Guttenburg *on New Year's Day 1861.*

It was on New Year's Day 1861 . . . that a most tragic wreck took place resulting in the drowning of a Deal pilot, Henry Pearson, as well as twenty-three others, including six women. In thick fog accompanied by snow driven before a near hurricane force wind, the Hamburg brig *Guttenburg* of 170 tons went on to the South Sand Head and later capsized. It was fortunate that the wreck had not occurred half an hour earlier when the *Guttenburg* was carrying fourteen survivors from the *Canton* which had been found dismasted and water-logged off the coast of Newfoundland. By chance the Walmer lugger *Cosmopolite* had fallen in with the German vessel off Dover and at her captain's request, since food supplies were now very low, had relieved him of the shipwrecked crew. After the *Guttenburg*

Shipwrecked sailors saved by safety beacon erected on the Goodwin Sands in 1840

'A Sharp Look Out', Deal. Early 1900s

Deal, Kent by E. Pritchett

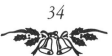

struck, several distress signals were fired but in the exceptionally poor visibility these went unnoticed except by a small handful of watchers on the beach at Deal, so that Ramsgate and all three lightvessels were for a time unaware of the disaster. A Deal boatman, Stephen Pritchard, telegraphed Ramsgate to ask for the lifeboat to be launched and within minutes both the *Northumberland* and the *Aid* were ready for sea. Then, to everyone's astonishment, Capt. Shaw, the Ramsgate harbourmaster, refused them permission to leave. His decision was based on the commissioners' inflexible rule that the lifeboat was not to go to sea unless specifically signalled or summoned by any one of the lightvessels, or a vessel was actually seen to be in distress. Since in this case the fog made it impossible for the Ramsgate men to see either the North Sand or Gull lights, let alone the South Sand, they argued strongly that the word of a responsible local boatman should be trusted but the harbourmaster was adamant. With the wind onshore from the north-east the sea state prevented any of the luggers, and presumably the Walmer lifeboat as well, from being launched, so the only hope for the wreck lay in the *Northumberland*. For three long hours, from 6.30 until 9.30 p.m., the lifeboat crew pleaded for permission to leave but still the harbourmaster refused, despite two more telegrams from Deal confirming the incident. His only comment was to say: 'If you must go, then go in your own luggers', knowing full well that if this had been at all possible they would already have left.

Unbeknown to the Ramsgate men, an attempt had already been made from Dover to reach the crew of the *Guttenburg*, since a Mr Irons, presumably the local harbour-master, had sent a tug out to the South Sand but it had returned empty-handed, having failed to find the wreck. At last the Ramsgate harbourmaster heard the sound of distress guns fired from the southernmost of the Goodwin's lightvessels, whose crew had sighted the wreck when the snow had ceased and visibility had improved. The

Northumberland was quickly released but on arrival at the scene the Ramsgate men found the vessel smashed to pieces and her captain, Mr Pearson, the pilot, and twenty-two others dead. For some time it was thought that no one had escaped the wreck but in fact two had been rescued by a Dover boat and a further five had managed to reach port in their own small lifeboat in an utterly exhausted condition. A charge of neglect of duty was brought against Capt. Shaw for not sending assistance sooner but he maintained that he was only observing 'the regulations, or routine' and, since the trustees of Ramsgate harbour expressed their satisfaction with his conduct, the Board of Trade decided there was no call for an inquiry. Despite being exonerated by his superiors, Capt. Shaw suffered the humility of a widely distributed satire entitled 'Routine – a Tale of the Goodwins', which left no doubt as to the author's opinion on the matter.

from

Bygone Kent – 'A Christmas Mystery'

CARSON RITCHIE

The medieval Church in an attempt to popularize Christmas allowed lively anthems to replace plainsong in Latin and liturgical dramas in the language of the common people to be performed in churches at Christmastime. All members of society therefore, including the illiterate, were now offered an entertaining way to experience the Christmas story. Carson Ritchie has researched the production of medieval Kentish mystery plays and pageants at the Christmas period and that strange medieval phenomena, the Boy Bishop.

As Christmas approached in medieval Kent, everyone abandoned their everyday occupations and turned instead to the business of producing the Christmas plays. Miracle or mystery plays are known to have been produced in a large number of

The 'pageants' or floats upon which the plays were performed were very difficult to move

Kent towns and villages, which included the following: Appledore, Bethersden, Brookland, Canterbury, Folkestone, Great Chart, Ham Street, Herne, High Halden, Hythe, Lydd, New Romney, Rochester, Ruckinge, Stone, Wittersham and Wye.

All these places produced miracle plays, mystery plays or took part in the Festival of the Boy Bishop. So popular were plays and play acting that 'Playstool' is a common name for a piece of land in Kent. The 'playstool' or 'outdoor theatre' as we would now call it for the extremely enthusiastic 'theatre group' of New Romney may have been Crockhill or Crockley Green.

Mystery plays were different from miracle plays in that a mystery took its theme straight from the Bible. The Apocrypha was in medieval times considered to have the same validity as any of the books of the Bible. It keeps cropping up in mystery plays, such as the most popular of all Christmas plays, the nativity. In the nativity play, Joseph sends out for two midwives to take care of Mary during her childbirth. This is a detail drawn from the Apocrypha; it does not occur in the New Testament. Mysteries were above all concerned with the unfolding story of the Bible, the fulfilment of prophesy, and the central 'mystery' of the Redemption of the word, as accomplished by the Nativity, Passion and Resurrection.

Miracle plays, on the other hand, might be drawn from some miracle that occurs in Scripture, such as the proposed sacrifice of Isaac by Abraham, and his miraculous delivery. On the whole, though, a Kentish miracle play was much more likely to be concerned with the incidents surrounding the miracles of a later saint.

The best known Kentish miracle play was probably 'The Play of St Christina', which was performed regularly at Bethersden. It is one of only seven miracle plays performed in England whose titles have survived. Other Kent miracle plays included the 'Play of Abraham and Isaac'. This was performed annually in Canterbury by the Guild of St Dunstan's, whose churchwardens still had custody of the manuscript of the play as late as 1520. It is not being speculative to assume that shortly after that date, the Reformers destroyed this manuscript, along with everything else they could lay hands on that was connected with the mystery or miracle plays. Their motive for doing this was that not merely did the mysteries incorporate religious teaching from the Catholic point of view, they were also performed on the stage. There was nothing that the Puritan branch of the Reformers hated as much as the drama. They felt that religious teaching ought to be confined to the pulpit, and that every aspect of the theatre was the work of the devil.

The pastoral parts of Kent delighted in those sturdy country characters, the shepherds, in the nativity play

One Canterbury miracle play which miraculously managed to survive until 'far on in the reign of Queen Elizabeth', was the 'Pageant of St Thomas'. The word 'pageant' in this connection, by the way, means the double-decker movable stage which will be described in a moment. The St Thomas play was held annually on 29 December, the day of the saint's martyrdom. The 29th was the day after Innocents' Day, the date on which the festival of the Boy Bishop came to an end, and as this began on 6 December, it will be seen that playgoing, with the accompanying feasting and jollity, went on right through Christmastide in Canterbury, as indeed it did in Kent as a whole.

No script for the 'Pageant of St Thomas' has survived, any more than it has for any of the other Kentish plays. It is nonetheless possible to reconstruct the play in part, from the expenditure accounts. Apparently, St Thomas was killed on the stage, and then later appeared transfigured in glory in heaven. The principal actor was gorgeously robed, just like a real archbishop, and wore linen garments, an alb and mitre. All these clothes must have suffered when artificial blood streamed all over them during the martyrdom. The blood was brought on stage in 'a new leather bag' and all the robes of the archbishop had to be washed between performances. The costumes of the murderers were also very expensive. They wore real armour, which was forged specially for the play, and carried real swords, which had to be hired. The 'pageant', a cart on wheels, needed repair from time to time, including the provision of new wheels, after being dragged through the narrow streets by a workforce which included an extra team of four men.

'St Thomas' seems to have gone with a bang, if only because large amounts of gunpowder were consumed during the performance, no doubt to mark the entrance, or exit, of devils routed by the Saint.

One of the reasons why Kentish players were always sure of a large and appreciative audience was that they kept in practice right through the year. Passion plays would, for example, be performed at Easter, and also at Whitsun, when the audience of the New Romney players contributed the enormous sum of £12 6s 6d.

The town was in every way a remarkable drama centre. Spectators came from all over England to see the Passion play performed there, just as nowadays they might go to Oberammergau in Bavaria. But, whereas the Oberammergau play is performed solely by people from the village, Romney welcomed players from other parts of Kent. Players from Appledore, Bethersden, Folkestone and Lydd were welcome there. The Romney players also played away a good deal in other towns. Drama in Kent was obviously fertilized by cross-contacts and throve on competition. Lydd was another very active theatre town, whose players went on tour. The town was noted for its play of 'St George'. The chaplain of the Guild of St George at New Romney visited Lydd to watch a performance, with a view to producing a similar play at Lydd.

But there was one feature of New Romney too remarkable to be passed over. The town actually employed a woman playwright! In 1463 the jurats of Romney paid Agnes Ford 6s 8d for writing a Passion play: 'The Interludes of Our Lord's Passion'. Mistress Ford is not the only known woman writer of religious plays. A German nun called Hroswitha wrote six mystery plays in Latin. There is, however, no record that she ever got any of them on the boards.

Romney was still determined to mount lavish productions, be the cost what it may. The players spent £4 17s 5d on London-made costumes. John the Baptist's jacket; the cotton coat of Judas; twelve sheepskin overcoats, and beards and wigs for the extras and the Fool are mentioned.

At one time or another, the company purchased three

This Boy Bishop died in office and was buried in full canonicals

cartloads of longbows, painted escutcheons, at £1 each, ells of buckram, a gross of doublet laces, real gold, vermilion and green for scenery painting. There was even a live paschal lamb, dressed in ribbons and garlands. Waits, drummers and minstrels provided the musical accompaniment to the play.

At cathedral cities such as Canterbury and Rochester, the Christmas season was marked by the Boy Bishop Festival. This entertainment was so different from anything that exists today that it is difficult to say just what kind of theatrical representation it was. Perhaps the term 'impersonation' would best describe it. The Boy Bishop was a choir boy who impersonated the real bishop for three weeks. The rest of the choir became his prebendaries. It was a festival of youth, and specifically holy youth. It recalled Jesus sitting in the Temple among the doctors while He was a boy. It also recalled St Nicholas, the original 'boy bishop'. From his cradle the Saint had shown marvellous indications of piety, and had therefore been selected as the patron saint of boys.

Later, and much more dramatically, St Nicholas, who is, of course, our own Santa Claus, had saved the life of two children going to school. At Myra, where he was bishop, he had brought back to life two schoolboys, travelling to their school at Athens. They had been murdered by a cruel innkeeper, who had cut them up to be pickled and sold as pork. Divine inspiration revealed this crime to the Saint; he made the innkeeper confess, and the boys were restored to life – in one piece.

This legend, which must have given nightmares to any child compelled to travel far to school, was celebrated on the stage as the 'Miracle of St Nicholas', and in the cathedral by

St Nicholas was the patron of childhood, schooldays and the festive season of Christmas

the Boy Bishop's impersonation. He had to do everything a real bishop did, except say Mass. He was dressed in specially made vestments, with scaled down crozier and episcopal ring. It was all very grand, but he had to sing for his supper, by conducting a dramatic performance in which he, and his boy prebendaries, satirized the shortcomings of the cathedral clergy of the day. He would deliver a sermon, in Latin probably, lead gorgeous processions, and if the occasion arose, entertain royalty with recitals of poems or songs, or dances. Being chosen as Boy Bishop meant that he was popular with his fellow choristers, and also a good singer, or he could never have filled the role successfully. If he did well, he was sure of being sent to university, or promoted to some cathedral office. If he died during office, he was buried in full pontificals under a sculptured tomb. On the 28 December he laid down his office, which meant that he could crowd into the audience, just like anyone else, on the following day for the St Thomas Martyrdom play.

Scenes with lots of devils in them, like this one in 'The Fall of Lucifer', called for a lot of gunpowder and sulphur for stage effects

Whereas the Boy Bishop Festival took place in or round the cathedral, those Kent plays which were not staged on a 'playstool' or open green were enacted on a moving stage which stopped in every principal street, usually before a building or landmark, such as the town cross. The pageant or movable stage required great force to get it moving, or for that matter to slow it when going downhill. Sometimes the wheels were greased with tallow or soap; a carpet of rushes was laid before them to let them bite. As the pageant ground to a halt the actors, who had dressed on the lower deck, would climb onto the top deck to deliver their play. As they drew towards the last line, messengers would hurry to the pageants in front or behind, which were going to stage other acts of the play, and arrange for them to move into sequence.

The drama historian A.S. Pollard estimated that the destruction of miracle plays in southern England by the puritan iconoclasts had amounted to some 140,000 lines of verse. There is no reason to suppose that the Kentish miracle plays were not among the very best ever written. Yet, if much was lost much was gained as well. In Canterbury Cathedral a stained glass window long portrayed the descent into Hell by Christ to rescue sinners; a scene from a miracle play. Chaucer drops allusions to the miracle plays in the Kentish setting of the *Canterbury Tales*. His miller, for example, has trod the boards as Herod. Shakespeare too must have watched the mystery plays during his touring days.

The age of the miracle plays was indeed a little miracle in itself, one in which communities strove not in emnity or rivalry, but in friendly emulation, as to who should put on the best play. Herne players thought nothing of crossing the county from north to south to play in New Romney, no matter how bad or dangerous the roads might be. The jurats of Lydd were prepared to help their great rivals, the Romney men, by selling them copes and vestments from their wardrobe.

Throughout all Kent, the greatest harmony and good feeling prevailed, for a community at odds with itself could never have hoped to put on a miracle play. Amidst feasting and dancing, the citizens and their wives went off to enjoy the spectacle they had done so much to create, even if it were only by contributions from their purse. For the whole festive season everybody was happy. And nobody wanted a White Christmas as it would make the wheels of the pageants slip.

The Great Snow

H.E. BATES

H.E. Bates (1905–74) though not a native of Kent, settled at Little Chart Forstal in 1931 where he wrote a number of books and short stories which have as their inspiration the Kent countryside. His best known works are probably those which feature the outrageously ebullient Larkin family whose opinion of Kent is that it is 'just perfick'. In contrast, this essay The Great Snow *is a perceptive and poetic evocation of countryside in the grip of severe winter conditions.*

For the third year in succession winter fell on the same day. The long, wild, rainy autumn, the days of flying brown leaves herded by warm, wet sea-winds, broke at last on the Saturday before Christmas. The wind swung north: by afternoon it was very cold: by Sunday it was bitterly cold. By Monday the ponds were covered with ice that would bear, and by Tuesday there was snow. In 1939 it was snow such as no one had seen in England, so continuously at least and for so long, for fifty years and, in many places, for a hundred years.

That year there were many berries on the holly; in spring the trees everywhere had been covered by clusters of green – white, pink-touched blossom. There had been many berries, too, on the hawthorns, and there was a tree that stood claret-covered until the last week of December. The cold did not begin reluctantly, as it often does in England, but suddenly and bitterly and fiercely. It bit down on the earth like teeth. It bit with a black and scarring effect, so that the earth seemed skinned raw by wind and frost and the trees were bared down to the black bone of the branches. Then it began to snow with that mournful, silent beauty, steadily and relentlessly, that only a great storm of snow can give. There are sometimes wild and brief snows which merely pepper the ploughed land into bars of whiteness and shadow. But this snow covered everything. It came down without a break for a whole day, then for another day, and then for still another. For seventy-two hours, a day and night, it drove down on a bitter wind from a sky that seemed solid with dirty grey clouds as far as heaven itself. Almost always after great snow the sky clears. It becomes cloudless, more blue than summer, sun and snow dazzling as light from a flashed mirror. But now the sky showed no sign of clearing. The clouds remained thick and sombre, dirty as a vast sheepskin. For a day there was intense frost, then a thaw, then frost again, but the sky did not change. It remained always that sombre and dirty grey, as if it had in it a vast world of unfallen snow.

And everywhere the fallen snow was magnificent. Sometimes snow in England is a local story; this snow was a national epic. It piled deep in woods and lay like heavy froth on shrubs

and trees. It filled to the brim the narrow roads that are carved in the steep sides of the downlands, so that they were still like rivers of snow running down the hill-sides long after the surrounding land was dark and unfrozen again and even touched with flowers. On the ridge below the Downs it drove through the hedgerows as if through gauze, and piled up on the western and southern sides of them in vast elongated drifts that blocked lanes and roads like miniature ranges of snow alps. The shapes carved by wind driving falling snow, and then by wind driving in bitter misty blizzards the light powder-snow refined by frost, were of fantastic splendour. They rolled away from the hedgerows like sea-waves of white marble. These waves were barbarously ridged, sharp-crusted, edged like knives. They were tipped with long and delicate curves which became overhanging eaves, making caves below. They were rippled like gigantic muscles of marble and into light branchings that were fringed like goose-feathers. They were as long and sharp as spears or as huge and deep and impassable as dunes of the purest snowsand. Wherever there were turns of road in high places, a bank, a hedge, a fence on the corner of unsheltered land, these drifts were whipped by ground blizzards into barriers of fantastic and lovely marble.

At intervals it snowed again. The nights were bitter: thirty degrees, thirty-five degrees, almost up to forty. The lake, on which no one had skated for thirty years, was hard and solid as a billiard-table. For one-and-sixpence we bought two pairs of clumsy but excellent pre-Great War German skates for the two girls, then only seven and five, and in two days they were striking out. You could skate every day and all day, and you wondered what sort of skater you would make if winters like this were suddenly to come to England every year. You began to be proficient at back-skating, inside edges and outside edges. You began to try swallow glides and inside edges backwards. You began to be very proud. You rested on your skates and looked down into the thick, clear ice and saw the fish lying still under the ice, and you realized that for once you were freer in their own element than they were. Then you got a book on skating. It was Victorian and academic and classically high class. The skaters illustrated in the act of doing perfect inside edges looked like professors or country doctors or Dr Grace laying down the law about the last ball of the over. You studied this book all evening and realized at the end of several hours that you could not skate at all. You never had been able to skate; all you were doing was wrong. If any skater of ability at all were ever to see you skating, it was extremely likely he would die of apoplexy. You were simply a windmill. It would clearly be better if you were to forget all you ever thought you knew and begin all over again. So, the next morning you took the book down to the ice. You put on your skates and consulted the book: page 47, Fig. 1, the forward inside edge. You carefully struck the correct attitude and prepared to proceed according to the highest Victorian standards in the art of figure-skating. You proceeded and promptly fell down and sprained your ankle.

That was the end of skating. The next day the snow came down fiercely and heavily again. Once more the blizzards drove through the hedges, piling up into the barbarous, beautiful drifts in the deep southern roads. And again, when the snow had fallen, the wind whipped it off the land in white salt-clouds that in turn piled into finer, sharper drifts. The sky still did not clear, but remained always the colour of a dirty sheepskin. It was now mid-January, and the holly-trees and hawthorns, scarlet and claret only a month before with a million berries, were now stripped black and naked. The birds were suffering greatly. Rooks herded together in oak trees, holding funereal conferences on the strange state of emergency, sending out only an occasional solitary patrol to survey the land. Pigeons came down on the gardens, stripping every cabbage-stalk down to the level of the snow. It was hard to say what was happening to the smaller birds, but when spring came it was clear that thousands had died. There were fewer nests, and it was known that here and there whole species had been almost wiped out. But they were to suffer more than from frost and snow and ice-wind and blizzard. A phenomenon common enough on the American continent, but fairly rare in England – ice rain – swept across the country, turning telegraph wires into cables of ice-rope, trees into skeletons of glass. It was at this time that birds were frozen to branches as they roosted or had their wings frozen to their bodies.

Between mid-January and the end of February there seemed to be scarcely a day when snow was not on the ground or falling or about to fall. Winter in England is rarely continuous, but now it was continuous and deadly. The English are bred to rapid climatic changes, and the snow, falling and lying for weeks on end, had a strange effect on character. It made people at once raw, touchy and depressed. Snow with sun, with the dazzling illumination that only sun and blue sky can give, is a bearable and beautiful thing, but now we had weeks of snow without sun, and the days had an imprisoning and unbearable effect. In the country there was also an effect of isolation. Buses ceased running, the arterial roads were beaten by traffic into corrugated switchbacks. Snow-ploughs, horse-drawn or drawn, perhaps, by a slow orange tractor, drove passages along secondary roads, and gangs of men cut gulleys where snow-ploughs stopped. But no sooner were passages and gulleys cut than it snowed again, and finally, in the third-class roads and the lanes, the snow-ploughs ceased altogether. Here the drifts remained piled above the hedges, high as the head of a man, untouched, in many cases, except by birds' feet or the threepointed prints of rabbits. Only the sun cleared them at last, many weeks later, and in the deep, sunless bends they remained unthawed until March. Still later, on a warm, sunlit afternoon when the countryside was green again and the young winter-wheat was rising at last after weeks of snow, we drove towards the Downs to look for primroses that bloom early there under the steep chalk banks in the shelter of giant beeches. As I turned the car to take the deep, narrow road that runs up the hill-side, I stopped in amazement. For there before me the drifts of snow, deep as the car-wheels, remained unmelted, shining like frosted glass in the sun.

Hengist's Daughter and the Wassail Cup

A re-telling by Fran Doel of the story from Geoffrey of Monmouth's History of the Kings of Britain *and William Lambarde's* Perambulation of Kent.

The story of how the fifth-century British ruler Vortigern employed Saxon mercenaries under the leadership of Hengist and allowed them to live in Kent is recounted both by the ninth-century Welsh monk Nennuius and by the Anglo-Saxon Chronicle. *In his Latin* History of the Kings of Britain (c. *1137), Geoffrey of Monmouth describes how the alliance was cemented by a marriage between Vortigern and Hengist's daughter Reinwin (in later sources called Rowena).*

According to Geoffrey's account, Reinwin greeted Vortigern with the Germanic toast 'Wassail' which means 'be whole' (i.e. healthy). This incident is drawn on by later Kent chroniclers such as William Lambarde in his Perambulation of Kent *(1570) as the legendary origin in Britain of the Christmas custom of wassailing, when festive toasts of cider, ale, punch or mulled-wine were drunk from a wassail bowl at feasts or in procession from house to house by bands of wassailers.*

· A Kent Christmas ·

As in the West Country, there are early records in Kent of cider-apple trees being wassailed – i.e. having a libation of cider poured over them and a song or rhyme sung or recited to them. Edward Hasted in his History of Kent *wrote: 'there is an odd custom fused in these parts about Keston and Wickham; a number of young men with a most hideous noise run into the orchards, and encircling each tree pronounce these words: 'Stand fast root, bear well top; Give us a youling sop, Every twig, apple big, Every bough, apple enough'.*

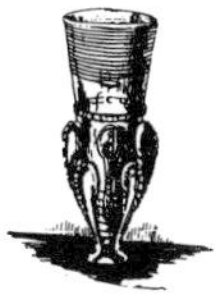

The British king, Vortigern, threatened by invasions from the Picts in the first half of the fifth century, hired Saxon mercenaries to protect his kingdom. As a reward, the king granted the Saxons territory in the neighbourhood of Lindney. But Hengist, the Saxon leader, was crafty. He saw that Vortigern's position was still not secure and suggested that yet more Saxon mercenaries should be brought in to consolidate Vortigern's position. In addition, he proposed that he himself should be rewarded for his services with the title of Earl or Prince.

Vortigern was reluctant to reward an outsider in this way 'I am forbidden to give you gifts of that sort' said the King, 'for you are a pagan and a foreigner. Even if I could look upon you as a fellow citizen I could never contemplate giving you something which would be disapproved of by the princes of my realm.'

'Nevertheless you command all my loyalty' said Hengist. 'You are and will ever by my lord. Grant me as much land as can be encircled by a single thong, and permit me to build a fortress there into which I can retreat in times of danger.'

Vortigern was swayed by Hengist's speech and permitted messengers to be sent to Germany. And Hengist took the hide of a great bull and cut the whole into a single thong and with this he encircled a high site in which he had a fortress constructed. The site took its name from the thong with which it had been measured and was ever afterwards known as Thanceastre in Saxon [modern Thanet].

And eighteen ships arrived in Britain each one containing carefully picked German soldiers. And Hengist's daughter Rowena also came over from Germany and her beauty was second to none. Once the soldiers had landed, Hengist invited Vortigern to inspect his new fortress home and they entertained the British king with a great banquet. And while he was feasting Rowena entered the hall from an inner room and she was carrying a golden goblet full of wine. She bowed low before Vortigern and said 'Laverd King, was hail!' Vortigern was entranced by the girl's beauty and he desired her. He asked his interpreter what it was that she had said and what he ought to reply. 'She called you Lord King' said the interpreter, 'and honoured you by drinking your health. What you should answer in reply is "drinc hail"!' This was said and the King ordered Rowena to drink from the goblet. Then he took the goblet from her hand, embraced her warmly and drank in his turn. And from that day to this it has been the tradition in Britain that the first to drink at a banquet calls out 'was hail!' to his partner and the next to drink replies 'drinc hail'.

As the banquet progressed, Vortigern became intoxicated both with wine and with desire for Rowena. He begged that the girl be given to him as a wife, and took no consideration of the fact that she was a pagan and he a Christian.

Hengist withdrew to confer with his brother Horsa and other senior Germans in the party. They discussed how they might profit from the King's request. It was agreed unanimously that the girl should be handed over to the King but that in exchange for her they should be given the province of Kent.

No time was wasted. Rowena was given to Vortigern and the province of Kent to Hengist (this last without the knowledge of the Earl who ruled the territory). That same night the King was married to the pagan girl and she pleased him beyond all measure. And by this action Vortigern incurred the enmity of his leaders and indeed his own sons, for he was the father of three boys whose names were Vortimer, Katigern and Paschent.

from

Bygone Kent – 'Fattening the Chickens'

ANNIS CUMFREY

Kent, like the rest of England during and after the First World War had suffered severe conditions and deprivation. But by 1925 there was a gradual improvement in economic conditions in the south, as can be ascertained from these cheerful reminiscences of Annis Cumfrey, a butcher's daughter from the village of Brasted near Sevenoaks in west Kent who remembers her childhood Christmases between the wars.

The author, aged three, with her parents in front of the shop in 1924

I have always enjoyed those days immediately before, particularly Christmas Eve, far more than the Day itself. As early as I can remember (at around three years old, I suppose) the December mornings were firmly mixed up with the sound of cockerels crowing in the early darkness.

My father kept chickens, both for egg production and to sell for the table, in the fields across towards Westerham to the south of Brasted Church and the selected cocks and young hens would be brought down in crates on the horse-drawn van to our yard for a final fattening-up early in the month. In those days many people in the village would set eggs under an extra hen and the resulting male birds would be kept at the end of the cottage gardens during the summer to sell to the butcher just before the Christmas trade to provide the family with some extra spending money for special seasonal treats. Therefore there were always a good many birds, in addition to the usual quota of 'layers', in the yard at the back of the shop and the cocks would start their challenge at an early hour. Oddly, there were very few fights among the birds but I suppose they were all in excellent condition at their young peak and about equally matched so, sensibly, they seldom chose to put matters to the test by actually fighting.

All the turkeys, as well as the few geese still required by traditionalists, came from Smithfield Market and the Ford van would set out around 4.00 a.m. so Father could make his selection and bring them back to fulfil the many orders. He always liked to bid for at least one of the prize-winning bullocks at the Sevenoaks Fat Stock show and the carcass, complete with prize card and rosette, would take pride of place in 'our show' where all the meat and poultry would be carefully arranged outside the shop under the 'pentiss' – an iron shelter supported on pillars over a tiled area in front of the open shop front. There were strong wooden shutters, latticed at the top section, to slide into place when we were shut, but Father was insistent that all butchers' premises should have a strong healthy draught of fresh air blowing through. Summer and winter the rear door into the yard stood wide open and the internal glass shutters were never used. All the shopmen wore layers of clothing under their smocks and blue and white striped aprons and my eldest sister, working in the little partitioned-off office, wore woollen gloves on her chillblained hands and kept her feet in a leather fur-lined footmuff! Father always seemed absolutely impervious to cold and would seldom wear his dark overcoat when going out; it, like his leather gloves, was kept exclusively for funerals!

This outside show, complete with greenery, was completely covered by a large tarpaulin at night and sometimes an elderly, very small and rather timid man would act as a sort of nightwatchman. I think the village must have been extremely honest as nothing ever seemed to go missing.

It was a busy time and, lying in my warm bed in a room

The Christmas show in 1923

overlooking the yard, I would hear sounds of great activity early and late, particularly when the hundreds of pounds of beef and pork sausages were being made in the pickle-room, so called because of the two great tanks of brine kept there for preparing salt beef, tongues and picklepork. Looking back, I think it would have reduced a modern Factory Inspector to hysterical tears as there was a powerful electric Hobard sausage-making machine with, as I remember, no sort of guards whatsoever. The room's polished brass light switch gave a very sharp shock each time it was turned on and anyone liable to be called upon to make a batch of sausages in the early afternoon darkness always had a piece of india rubber in their pocket, kept especially for use when working the switch. Many extra sausages had to be made, as a pack was often added to customers' Christmas orders as a gift.

A good deal of slaughtering would go on in the big thatched

roof slaughter-house (now the site of a cedarwood antiques emporium) and the head slaughterman and his assistants – they were all kindly men, very fond of animals and splendid at playing nursemaid to me – would work late into the evening fortified with many plates of thick paste sandwiches and jugs of hot, sweet tea prepared by my mother – Dick always had jam ones as he distrusted paste!

I would listen sleepily in the mornings for the sound of the quarters of beef, hanging from big hook on the iron rail which went round the shop, being moved along with the aid of the 'longarm', a wooden pole finely polished by years of meat fat and handling, which was topped by an iron gadget. You will be glad to know we *did* have an icebox, a room in the centre of the building with thick double walls insulated with sawdust between and containing a tank full of great blocks of ice delivered from London by lorry . . . . Father was always of the opinion that the weather invariably became warm during the last days before 23 December especially to bedevil the butchers!

All the families who regularly purchased meat from us were anxious to hear how much money they had saved in our Christmas Club, although they usually knew to a ha'penny. All their 'paying-ins' were carefully recorded and everyone was duly notified of the amount standing to their credit in the book. We had a small notice – celluloid on metal, I suppose – which announced 'Our Christmas Club has now commenced. Join at once'.

Another gentle excitement was our Christmas Draw which would have a turkey, chickens, beef, pork and sausages as prizes. Hundreds of tickets would be sold and Father was terribly scrupulous about the whole thing, adding another prize as we dashed up to Mrs Davis at the newspaper shop for a further supply of raffle ticket books. It was drawn in the kitchen a day or so before Christmas Eve, late in the evening with all the carefully folded counterfoils in a big basket, and we usually dragged in a couple of locals who would, just by chance, be waiting outside the closed shop, to assist in the ritual and, it was tacitly understood, to see everything was fair and all above board.

A great deal of hard work went in to getting up all the orders but Father and Mother always managed to have everything done so that during the afternoon of Christmas Eve a little quiet entertaining of close friends might take place in the living room which had a door opening straight into the shop.

Christmas Day would come at last. I was a fortunate brat; being very much the youngest of the family I seemed to have more than my fair share of elderly relatives and they, as well as friends of my parents, would give me presents. In those days many gifts came by post, the truly wonderfully exciting 'brown paper packages tied up with string' which feature among Julie Andrews' 'favourite things'. One year, I remember, I was given two really beautiful doll's teasets. One was plain pale brown listre and the other was quite large, cream with gilding and blue transfer-printed landscape pictures on each piece.

We would always have a pair of chickens, complete with stuffing, sausages, breadsauce and brussels sprouts, followed by pudding and custard for dinner at one o'clock, tea with celery, bread and butter and Christmas Cake at five, not to mention a substantial supper at nine. In between there were lots of apples, oranges, tangerines, chestnuts, etc, plus mincepies which nobody ever wanted. Where did we put it all? Another item which always had pride of place on the sideboard was a big pineapple. This was a tradition in my father's family and, presumably, had been for as long as the pineapple had been available to the comfortably-off Kentish farmer and tradesman. One year, probably about 1931, the price of a large South African pineapple rose to 12s 6d, then also the cost of a bottle of Scotch, and my incensed parent swore that was the end. He weakened of course and dashed off to Sevenoaks at the last minute to buy one as usual, because, as far as he was concerned, it just would not have been Christmas without a pineapple.

from

The Nativity of Jesus Christ

A MEMBER OF THE KENTISH SOCIETY

A native of Kent will call himself either a Man of Kent or a Kentish Man depending on whether he was born east or west of that great tributary of the Thames, the River Medway. Roughly speaking, those who are born or live east of the River Medway are Men of Kent while those that are native to west of the Medway take the title Kentish Men. Societies have existed of each group for hundreds of years and this eighteenth-century poem, which was published in a local paper, the Maidstone Journal, *on Christmas Day 1787 was written by a man who chose only to identify himself by the title 'A Member of the Kentish Society'.*

Crib: The Friars, Aylesford

An Angel came, sent from the throne supreme,
The Saviour's natal morning to proclaim;
Fear not, said he, to cheer each human mind,
Tidings of joy to you and all mankind;
I bring from mansions of eternal bliss,
Prime source of all terrestial happiness:
This day, a Saviour's born of David's line,
In David's town, and this shall be the sign;
'The babe, you'll find to save mankind decreed,
In swaddling bands, and where brute oxen feed
Laid in a manger, earth cannot afford
A bed t'accommodate its Sovereign Lord,
Who at his birth, his godlike power to prove,
Each mimic god, to irate oblivion drove;
A host celestial, cloth'd with robes of light,
With joy replete, began their rapid flight
And through th'eternal portal from above,
Rush'd down to earth to sing redeeming love.'

The Hooden Horse – an East Kent Christmas Custom

PERCY MAYLAM

Mid-winter rituals of dressing up as horses and horned animals are widespread in Britain and are undoubtedly of pagan origin. In Kent in the seventh century, Archbishiop Theodorus decreed penance for three years for those 'who transformed themselves into the semblance of wild animals . . . at the kalends of January . . . because this is devilish.'

Despite this the custom of 'hoodening', in which a man disguised himself as a horse by crouching under a sacking cover holding a pole with a carved wooden horse's head attached to it, survived in the Isle of Thanet, Deal and Walmer into the early twentieth century. The horse was traditionally accompanied by a Waggoner, Jockey, Mollie (a man disguised as a woman with blackened face and with a besom broom) and musicians, though as the custom declined, the number of participants shrank also. In Thanet the Hoodeners visited farms over the Christmas period; in Walmer and Deal they visited shops (open until 8 p.m. on Christmas Eve), pubs and hotel bars. Naomi

Wiffen, writing to us from Edenbridge in the early 1980s, remembered seeing the Hooden Horse at Deal as a girl:

> *I remember as a child being taken out on Christmas Eve to the High Street in Deal where the shops would be open very late, and it was the only time Deal children were allowed out in the evening, as parents were very strict. As we would be looking at the lighted shops, and listening to the people selling their wares, a horrible growl, and a long horse's face would appear, resting on our shoulder and when one looked round, there would be a long row of teeth snapping at us with its wooden jaws. It was frightening for a child. Usually, there would be a man leading the horse, with a rope, and another covered over with sacks or blanket as the horse.*

In recent years, Hooden horses have been revived at Whitstable and St Nicholas-at-Wade and a first West Kent Hooden Horse has appeared with the Tonbridge Mummers regularly at Christmas.

Percy Maylam, a Canterbury solicitor, wrote the classic book on the Hooden Horse in a numbered edition in 1909. He first came across the Hooden Horse when spending Christmases with his uncle at Gore Street, Monkton from 1888–92. In preparation for the book he photographed the Hoodeners at St Nicholas-at-Wade in 1905, Walmer in 1906 and Deal 1907 as well as doing extensive research in newspaper archives.

Anyone who has spent a Christmas in a farm-house in Thanet – it has been my good fortune to spend five – will not forget Christmas Eve; when seated round the fire, one hears the banging of gates and tramping of feet on the gravel paths outside (or, if the weather be seasonable, the more cheerful crunching of crisp snow), and the sound of loud clapping. Everybody springs up saying, 'The hoodeners have come, let us go and see the fun.' The front door is flung open, and there they all are outside, the 'Waggoner' cracking his whip and leading the Horse (the man who plays this part is called the 'hoodener'), which assumes a most restive manner, champing his teeth, and rearing and plunging, and doing his best to unseat the 'Rider', who tries to mount him, while the 'Waggoner' shouts 'whoa'! and snatches at the bridle. 'Mollie' is there also! She is a lad dressed up in woman's clothes and vigorously sweeps the ground behind the horse with a birch broom. There are generally two or three other performers besides, who play the concertina, tambourine or instruments of that kind. This performance goes on for some time, and such of the spectators as wish to do so, try to mount and ride the horse, but with poor success. All sorts of antics take place, Mollie has been known to stand on her head, exhibiting nothing more alarming in the way of lingerie than a pair of hobnail boots with the appropriate setting of corduroy trousers. Beer and largesse are dispensed and the performers go further. Singing of songs and carols is not usually a part of the performance and no set words are spoken. In Thanet, occasionally, but not always, the performers, or some of them, blacken their faces. Years ago, smock frocks were the regulation dress of the party.

In a house which possesses a large hall, the performers are often invited inside; at times the horse uses little ceremony, and opening the door, walks in uninvited . . . . Without doubt the Hoodeners are seen at their best outdoors – and in the court or on the lawn of some old farm-house, for then the eyes of the spectators coming fresh from the light inside take only an impressionist picture of the scene, and the horse in the

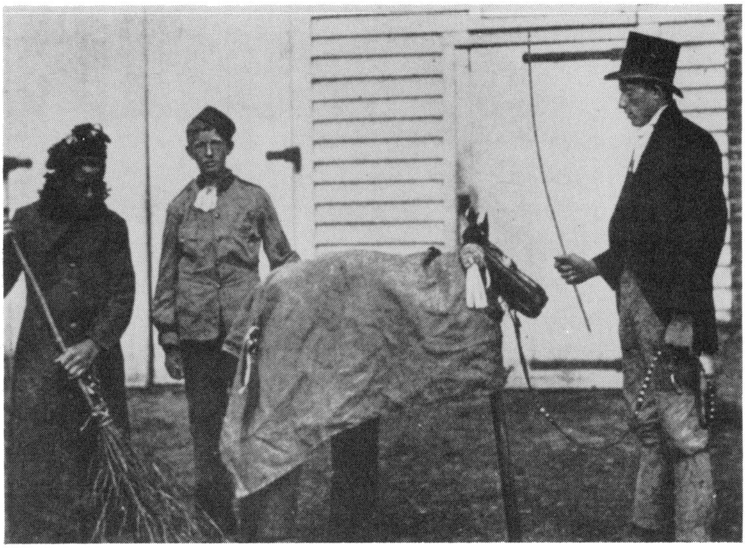

Hoodeners from Hale Farm, St Nicholas-at-Wade, 1905

dim winter's night, made even more indistinct by occasional cross rays of flickering light from the windows, becomes a monster of weird and awesome possibilities.

In 1905 Maylam photographed a team of Hoodeners from Hale farm, St Nicholas-at-Wade, where they were employed in looking after horses; the team consisted Horse, Rider, Waggoner, Mollie and two musicians. His description of the horse follows:

> The ears are pointed pieces of leather. The head is decorated with all the trappings usual in the case of a Kent farm horse in that district when dressed in state. On the top of the head, between the ears, with a swinging disc, is the head brass, and on the forehead the circular brass ornament called the face piece . . . the tail is made

Hoodeners at Walmer, 1906

of a small piece of horsehair decorated with caytis. The bridle is a long piece of leather thickly covered with brass studs.

On Christmas Eve, 1906, I went to Walmer, and having ascertained the time when the party would set out, I had a comfortable tea at the hotel near Walmer Station. While at tea, a man in grotesque attire came into the room, and proceeded to blacken his face with burnt cork at the fire. I, who had thoughts for nothing but hoodening, enquired if he were one of that party, 'No,' he said, and it appeared he was one of the Walmer minstrels with no very great opinion of such obsolescent customs as hoodening.

However, very shortly afterwards, the well-known clap! clap! was heard from within the bar – the Hoodeners had come. I hastened to see them. The party consisted of four: the hoodener with the horse's head, the man whose duty it is to lead the horse, and when not doing so, to play the triangle, and two musicians, one playing the tambourine and the other the concertina . . . . Here I found the practice was that the 'gratuity' had to be placed in the horse's jaws, and . . . the horse put his head on the counter of the bar while the landlord's little daughter was lifted up from the other side in order to carry out the proper form of giving the money, after conquering her fright, real or feigned.

. . . Mr Robert Laming told me . . . that he had been out with his horse on Christmas Eve for this five and twenty years and missed doing so only one year. The Walmer party were in their ordinary clothes, but formerly, I was told, they wore smock frocks; they had no Mollie, nor any recollection of her. I accompanied the party a little way on their rounds which I was told would not finish till about eleven o'clock: it was then six-thirty, and I found the Hoodeners sure of their welcome, the horse gambolled into all the crowded shops, and at Christmas they are crowded, and every one was pleased except a collie dog which worked himself into a fearful rage but feared to try his teeth against the wooden jaws of the horse. On visiting the butcher, he, regardless of the graminivorous habits of the animal, placed a mutton chop in the jaws besides the accustomed tribute, a piece of humour which met with great applause.

from

Hughes the Wer-Wolf – 'The Ashford Wer-Wolf's Christmas Dinner'

SUTHERLAND MENZIES

In the Middle Ages, European legends of men who were periodically transformed into the likeness of wolves were commonplace. These tales lingered longest in eastern Europe, France and Germany; in Britain they died out with the extinction of the wolf, though the name 'wer-wolf' is Anglo-Saxon meaning 'man-wolf'. With the revival of imaginative writing in the nineteenth century, such legends were given a fresh impetus and provided material for the gothic horror writers.

Sutherland Menzies is the pseudonym of Elizabeth Stone who wrote this story of a Kentish wer-wolf about 1838 and claimed it was based on a Kentish legend. The author points out in a footnote that 'Hugh, surnamed

Lupus, the first Earl of Kent, bore for his crest a wolf's head.' What she doesn't mention is that the symbol of a wolf's head often represented an outlaw and need have nothing to do with wer-wolves. The hero of her story is only pretending to be a wer-wolf.

It was chill winter – Christmas-tide – the distant toll of the curfew had long ceased, and all the inhabitants of Ashford were safe housed in their tenements for the night. Hughes, solitary, motionless, silent, his forehead grasped between his hands, his gaze dully fixed upon the decaying brands that feebly glimmered upon his hearth: he heeded not the cutting north wind, whose sweeping gusts shook the crazy roof, and whistled through the chinks of the door; he started not at the harsh cries of herons fighting for prey in the marsh, nor to the dismal croaking of the ravens perched over his smoke-vent. He thought of his departed kindred, and imagined that his hour to join them would soon be at hand; for the intense cold congealed the marrow of his bones, and fell hunger gnawed and twisted his entrails. Yet, at intervals, would a recollection of nascent love of Branda to suddenly appease his else intolerable anguish, and cause a faint smile to gleam across his wan features.

'Oh, blessed, Virgin! grant that my sufferings may speedily cease!' murmured he, despairingly. 'Oh, would I might be a wer-wolf, as they call me! I could then requite them for all the foul wrong done me. True, I could not nourish myself with their flesh; I would not shed their blood; but I should be able to terrify and torment those who have wrought my parents' and sisters' death – who have persecuted our family even to extermination! Why have I not the power to change my nature into that of a wolf, if, of a verity, my ancestors possessed it, as they avouch? I should at least find carrion to devour, and not die thus horribly. Branda is the sole being in this world who cares for me; and that conviction alone reconciles me to life!'

Hughes gave free current to these gloomy reflections. The smouldering embers now emitted but a feeble and vacillating light, faintly struggling with the surrounding gloom, and Hughes felt the horror of darkness coming strong upon him; frozen with the ague-fit one instant, and troubled the next by the hurried pulsation of his veins, he arose, at last, to seek some fuel, and threw upon the fire a heap of faggot-chips, heath and straw, which soon raised a clear and crackling flame. His stock of wood had become exhausted, and seeking wherewith to replenish his dying hearth-light, whilst foraging under the rude oven amongst a pile of rubbish placed there by his mother wherewith to bake bread – handles of tools, fractured joint-stools, and cracked platters, he discovered a chest rudely covered with a dressed hide, and which he had never seen before; and seizing upon it as though he had discovered a treasure, broke open the lid, strongly secured by a string.

This chest, which had evidently remained long unopened, contained the complete disguise of a wer-wolf – a dyed sheepskin, with gloves in the form of paws, a tail, a mask with an elongated muzzle, and furnished with formidable rows of yellow horse-teeth.

Hughes started backwards, terrified at his discovery – so opportune, that it seemed to him the work of sorcery; then, on recovering from his surprise, he drew forth one by one the several pieces of this strange envelope, which had evidently seen some service, and from long neglect had become somewhat damaged. Then rushed confusedly upon his mind the marvellous recitals made him by his grandfather, as he nursed him upon his knees during earliest childhood; tales, during the narration of which his mother wept silently, as he laughed heartily. In his mind there was a mingled strife of feelings and purposes alike indefinable. He continued his silent examination of this criminal heritage, and by degrees his imagination grew bewildered with vague and extravagant projects.

Hunger and despair conjointly hurried him away: he saw objects no longer save through a bloody prism: he felt his very teeth on edge with an avidity for biting: he experienced an inconceivable desire to run: he set himself to howl as though he had practised wer-wolfery all his life, and began thoroughly to invest himself with the guise and attributes of his novel vocation. A more startling change could scarcely have been wrought in him, had that so horribly grotesque metamorphosis really been the effect of enchantment; aided, too, as it was, by the fever which generated a temporary insanity in his frenzied brain.

Scarcely did he thus find himself travestied into a wer-wolf through the influence of his vestment, ere he darted forth from the hut, through the forest and into the open country, white with hoar frost, and across which the bitter north wind swept, howling in a frightful manner and traversing the meadows, fallows, plains, and marshes, like a shadow. But, at that hour, and during such a season, not a single belated wayfarer was there to encounter Hughes, whom the sharpness of the air, and the excitation of his course, had worked up to the highest pitch of extravagance and audacity: he howled the louder proportionally as his hunger increased.

Suddenly the heavy rumbling of an approaching vehicle arrested his attention; at first with indecision, then with a stupid fixity; he struggled with two suggestions, counselling him at one and the same time to fly and to advance. The carriage, or whatever it might be, continued rolling towards him; the night was not so obscure but that he was enabled to distinguish the tower of Ashford church at a short distance off, and hard by which stood a pile of unhewn stone, destined either for the execution of some repair, or addition to the saintly edifice, in the shade of which he ran to crouch himself down, and so await the arrival of his prey.

It proved to be the covered cart of Willieblud, the Ashford flesher, who was wont twice a week to carry meat to Canterbury, and travelled by night in order that he might be among the first at market-opening. Of this, Hughes was fully aware, and the departure of the flesher naturally suggested to him the inference that his niece must be keeping house by herself, for our lusty flesher had long been a widower. For an instant, he hesitated whether he should introduce himself there, so favourable an opportunity thus presenting itself, or whether he should attack the uncle and seize upon his viands. Hunger got the better of love this once, and the monotonous whistle with which the driver was accustomed to urge forward his sorry jade warning him to be in readiness, he howled in a plaintive tone, and, rushing forward, seized the horse by the bit.

'Willieblud, flesher,' said he, disguising his voice, and speaking to him in the 'lingua franca' of that period, 'I hunger; throw me two pounds of meat if thou would'st have me live.'

'St Willifred have mercy on me!' cried the terrified flesher, 'is it thou, Hughes Wulfric, of Wealdmarsh, the born wer-wolf?'

'Thou say'st sooth – it is I,' replied Hughes, who had sufficient address to avail himself of the credulous superstition of Willieblud; 'I would rather have raw meat than eat of thy flesh, plump as thou art. Throw me, therefore, what I crave, and forget not to be ready with the like portion each time thou settest out for Canterbury market; or, failing thereof, I tear thee limb from limb.'

Hughes, to display his attributes of a wer-wolf before the gaze of the confounded flesher, had mounted himself upon the spokes of the wheel, and placed his forepaw upon the edge of the cart, which he made semblance of snuffing at with his snout. Willieblud, who believed in wer-wolves as devoutly as he did in his patron saint, had no sooner perceived this monstrous paw, than, uttering a fervent invocation to the latter, he seized upon his daintiest joint of meat, let it fall to the ground, and whilst Hughes sprung eagerly down to pick it up, the butcher at the same instant having bestowed a sudden and violent blow upon the flank of his beast, the latter set off at a round gallop without waiting for any reiterated invitation from the lash.

Christmas at Leeds Castle

Spectacularly sited on an island which was once a Kentish thane's stronghold, Leeds Castle has seen more than nine hundred Christmases since its Norman foundation. Today the magnificent castle and parkland are preserved for the public benefit – for international medical seminars and for artistic and cultural events. At Christmastime there is a full and varied programme of traditional Christmas events with entertainments in which carollers, clowns and Kentish handbell-ringers known as the 'Handbell Hoodeners' entertain the guests. Warming soups, mulled wine and mince pies are always on hand. On New Year's Day a treasure trail is staged throughout the park.

We are indebted for the following accounts of Christmases past at Leeds Castle from the Marketing Manager, Mrs Joanna Oswin, from Mr David Clegget, Official Historian to Leeds Castle Foundation and to Mr John Money, who was agent to Lady Baillie (the last private owner) from 1926 to 1975.

During the 1950s Charles Wykeham Martin (1801–1970), owner of the castle, and Conway Robinson (1805–84), developed a close friendship through correspondence. Robinson was a founder member of the Virginia Historical Society in 1834 and for many years its corresponding secretary. In his

Christmas letter to Wykeham Martin of 1868 it is clear Robinson asked for details of Christmas customs in England at that time and earlier. On 12 January 1869 with castle and park wrapped in winter snow, Charles Wykeham Martin sat in his study overlooking the Gloriette and penned the following letter to his friend. It set before Robinson the customs, upstairs and downstairs, then enjoyed in Kent and also some which Wykeham Martin recalled from earlier days:

My Dear Sir,

I sent you *my* mother's Recipe for mince pies; which was considered a very good one – I do not know whether our present *artiste* uses it – I rather think she has one of her own with which we are very well satisfied. The Custom of having this delicacy at table lasts for several weeks at this Season, perhaps till the middle or end of February.

I think that *some* of the old Christmas dishes are not so favoured as they were when I was a boy. I do not often see brawn now. It is pork rolled up into a bag like a Stilton Cheese & inclosed in a heavy envelope which is I believe the skin of the breast of the animal. It is eaten with Vinegar mustard, salt & *sugar* made into a sauce on the plate of the person eating it. Egg-nog is called *Egg-flip* in Kent & the last time I attended a New Years' ball at Sevenoaks the custom of drinking it at Supper was generally followed by the company present. At Linton & Sevenoaks the *gentlemen* also ate oysters & drank beer, but I do not think this rough & ready custom survives. They remained behind after the ladies had returned to the drawing room for this enjoyment. It is very common to hang up a large branch of mistletoe from the ceiling & then the gentlemen claim the privilege of taking young ladies under it & giving them a salute: but this privilege is seldom exercised by the party upstairs. I believe the servants practise it still. A boar's head prepared like brawn used to be common. I also think that mulled elder wine, egg-flip & toasts & ale &c are now rather giving way. Since, after the reduction of the duty fair claret is to be had for 14/- (70p) a dozen. Formerly also a preparation of millet is now yielding to Sago. Tapioca & Semolina which are more palatable & very cheap – nevertheless the general spirit of keeping up Christmas shows a healthy vitality & turkeys continue to be immolated as the appropriate delicacy & barrels of oysters are a suitable gift. For the Children Christmas trees are provided & Christmas Pantomines & twelfth night parties are given both for young & old, Children's balls being very common at this time of the year. The Churches are gaily decorated with evergreens, particularly holly with its red berries & family gatherings are quite the order of the day.

I Subscribe myself
Ever most truly Yrs
Charles Wykeham Martin

Leeds Castle Jan 12. 1869.

LEEDS CASTLE RECIPE NO. 1
(the late Mrs W M)

Lemon mince meat
3lbs of raisins
3lbs of currants
2lbs & $\frac{1}{2}$ fresh suet finely shredded
1lb & $\frac{1}{2}$ powdered sugar
3 lemons peeled thin, the peel to be used, & the lemons boiled whole in cold water until they become quite tender, the juice to be extracted but *not* used, the pulp to be beaten into a paste & added to other ingredients.

$\frac{1}{4}$ oz cloves
1 oz of nutmeg
12 oz of candied orange & lemon peel mixed
Half a bottle of brandy
Half a bottle of port wine
Mix the mince meat well together.

RECIPE NO. 2, THIS IS THE ONE WE USE

Put in in equal weight
Raisins
Currants
Brown sugar suet
Apples
Lemon peel grated flavoured with spice
2 bottles of brandy & 2 of wine for 10lbs.
No. 1 Recipe we considered rather too rich.

Leeds Castle, Maidstone, Kent

Christmas at Leeds after the last war was very largely a purely family gathering. Lady Baillie, who had three half sisters and two daughters all within the same age bracket and all with children, would collect a very considerable clan around her, which also included a number of old family friends who came every year. It was unusual for a 'new face' to appear. The Christmas party usually lasted over the New Year.

Christmas decorations within the castle always followed the same pattern year by year. Vast paper chains and lanterns adorned all the reception rooms – giving them an air of the twenties and as if they had been decorated specially for children. The Christmas tree, traditionally adorned, was in the dining room and was always carefully selected so that it looked as if it was going through the ceiling. The 'spike' on the top was cut off and the surrounding small branches were against the ceiling to which was attached the 'fairy'. Poinsettias grown in the greenhouses were used in profusion throughout the house, grown on single stems and individual flowers as large as dinner plates. Those cut and used in vases had to have their water changed daily as the room temperatures were high and the water became warm. A complete bough of mistletoe hung over the doorway between the library and dining room. A well known character from the local timber firm came each year and climbed one of the highest lime trees overhanging the weir pond using climbing irons but no safety rope. He let down the entire cluster, nearly a yard across, on a string. He was rewarded with a £5 note and a pint of beer in the hostel. The main staircase had holly placed at the extremity of each step with tufts of cotton wool on it to simulate snow. Often hot house flowers, including forced bulbs, were used and the scent was at times almost overpowering. Holly always decorated the table for Christmas lunch and lily of the valley produced from frozen corns for Christmas night. Matins was compulsory for all staying in the house and the castle party usually filled at least the six front rows in the right-hand aisle.

The household staff had their Christmas dinner at midday and the dining room luncheon was a comparatively low key affair. The great event was Christmas night dinner. A member of the staff of those days remarked recently 'We worked hard and long hours but we enjoyed ourselves'. A sentiment seldom expressed today. There were usually nursery as well as dining room meals for the younger members of the party. On Boxing Day there was a 'boys' shoot', made up of any of the younger members of the family who were considered safe to handle a gun and a few adults, usually fathers. The keepers and a few beaters would turn out and it was a jolly affair. Anything that moved was considered fair game and one had to be pretty quick on one's feet at times. Other ventures included croquet if the weather was fine, walking in the grounds and visiting the aviaries and greenhouses. Calls were paid on retired staff members who were known to the house party.

Although the castle was usually empty of guests and family by that time, no single decoration was allowed to be removed before Twelfth night.

With every room full, children, dogs abounding, it was a time of great happiness with a great atmosphere of 'family'.

'The Seven Joys of Mary'

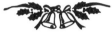

'The Seven Joys of Mary' is a very popular folk carol, extensively printed in broadsides in the eighteenth century and collected in the oral tradition in the south of England in the nineteenth and twentieth centuries. The concept of the seven joys was a part of the medieval adoration of the Virgin.

This unusual Kent version was contributed by folklore researcher Simon Evans. It was collected in Gravesend in the 1880s and was said to be 'a favourite with the Gravesend juveniles just before and at Christmas, when it may be repeatedly heard in the town and suburbs.' It is unusual in having Jesus 'ride above the sun' in the first verse and in wearing the crucifix instead of being on it in verse six.

The first good joy that Mary had,
It was the joy of one,
To see her own son Jesus,
To ride above the sun,

REFRAIN

To ride above the sun, good man,
And blessed may He be;
Both Father, Son, and Holy Ghost,
To all eternity.

The next good joy that Mary had,
It was the joy of two,
To see her own son Jesus,
To make the lame to go.

The next good joy that Mary had,
It was the joy of three.
When that her own son Jesus
Did make the blind to see.

The next good joy that Mary had,
It was the joy of four,
To see her own son Jesus,
To read the Scriptures o'er.

The next good joy that Mary had,
It was the joy of five,
To see her own son Jesus,
To raise the dead to life.

The next good joy that Mary had,
It was the joy of six,

To see her own son Jesus,
To wear the Crucifix.

The next good joy that Mary had
It was the joy of seven,
To see her own son Jesus,
To wear the crown of heaven.

Stained glass of All Saints Church, Maidstone

from

Folk in Kent – 'Santa Specials'

JORIS FIELD

The Romney, Hythe and Dymchurch Railway runs for nearly fourteen miles across the Romney Marsh, from the historic Cinque Port of Hythe, via the coastal resorts and former centres of smuggling at Dymchurch and New Romney, to Dungeness. It was opened in 1927 as 'The world's smallest public railway' and has a fleet of one-third full size steam and diesel locomotives, which run at speeds up to 25 mph on rails just 15 in apart.

The Santa Specials run most weekends in December up to Christmas and on these particular outings seats must be pre-booked. The Santa Specials run from Hythe to New Romney, where the children are met by Father Christmas. Every child receives a present and all the family can take seasonal cheer in the form of hot punch (made to an old railway recipe), sausage rolls and mince pies.

In this vivid article from Folk in Kent, *twelve year old Joris Field describes his 1989 Santa Special outing.*

In Holland, where my mother was born, the children have their Christmas presents earlier, on 6 December – St Nicholas'

Day. In the south-east of Kent Santa comes early as well, and has done for a number of years. In fact, he comes on a little steam engine called *The Bug* which has a coach behind it with his big sack of presents in it.

The day starts when you arrive at the Hythe station of the Romney, Hythe and Dymchurch Railway. You show your ticket and go on to the platform to wait for the train. Sometimes, if you are lucky, you might see your locomotive being turned round on the turntable and then being filled up with water. One of the two smart new diesels, recently added to the Nelson steam locos, pulled us this last Christmas, but it had the same sounding whistle that the steam ones do. When the loco is coupled to the train everyone gets in and not until the guard is sure that everyone is in does the train go.

We are soon off, through the cold, flat marshes, with the fields of sheep spending their winter there. The whistle blows as we speed through Dymchurch station, non-stop today, and on through the fields again until we gently halt at New Romney Station.

As we get out the cry goes up 'Here he comes!' A little steam locomotive – *The Bug* with a big Thomas the Tank Engine face on the front steam towards us on the other side of the platform. On it we see Father Christmas with red coat and a real white beard. (He admitted he grew it specially as last year's false one blew off.)

Everyone goes into the cafeteria and all the children queue up with their tickets, which have their name and age on, to get their present and a badge. Meanwhile, on the other side of the room the adults are queuing for mince pies, sausage rolls and drinks.

Before we go we visit the computer-controlled model railway – a fantastic layout. The whistle calls everyone back to the platform where the long train waits to take us back across Romney March to Hythe. When our train leaves, Santa drives his loco alongside the departing train, waving to eveyrone.

Nelson's Last Journey

WILLIAM BEATTY

On 21 October 1805, Horatio, Viscount Nelson, Admiral of the Fleet, died in action during the great British naval victory of Trafalgar. In order to preserve his body for a hero's lying in state and funeral, he was kept in brandy, leading to gruesome traditions preserved by Thomas Hardy that thirsty sailors had 'broached the admiral'.

A more scientific account of the preservation of the body during its journey to Spithead and then round the Sussex and Kent coast, is quoted below from the Authentic Narrative of the Death of Lord Nelson *by William Beatty, MD, Surgeon to the* Victory. *To this we have added an account of the* Victory *putting in to Broadstairs with its sad cargo just before Christmas. Nelson's body was at Greenwich (then of course in Kent) over Christmas and we have quoted some interesting details of the lying in state, boat journey through Kent to London and funeral procession from the Official Funeral Programme in St Paul's Cathedral Library.*

There was no lead on board to make a coffin: a cask called a leaguer, which is of the largest size on shipboard, was therefore chosen for the reception of the body, which, after the hair had been cut off, was stripped of the clothes except the shirt, and put into it, and the cask was then filled with brandy.

. . . At length the *Victory* arrived at Spithead, after a tedious passage of nearly five weeks from Gibraltar: and as no instructions respecting his Lordship's Remains were received at Portsmouth while the ship remained there, and orders being transmitted to Captain Hardy for her to proceed to the Nore, the Surgeon represented to him the necessity of examining the state of the Body; common report giving reason to believe that it was intended to lie in state at Greenwich Hospital, and to be literally exposed to the public. On the 11th of December therefore, the day on which the *Victory* sailed from Spithead for the Nore, Lord Nelson's body was taken from the cask in which it had been kept since the day after his death. On inspecting it externally, it exhibited a state of perfect preservation.

Nelson's funeral barge leaving Greenwich, January 1806. From *Life of Admiral Lord Nelson* by James Stavier Clarke and John M. Arthur

. . . The Remains were wrapped in cotton vestments, and rolled from head to foot with bandages of the same material, in the ancient mode of embalming. The body was then put into a leaden coffin, filled with brandy holding in solution camphor and myrrh. This coffin was inclosed in a wooden one, and placed in the after-part of His Lordship's cabin, where it remained till the 21st of December, when an order was received from the Admiralty for the removal of the Body. The coffin that had been made from the mainmast of the French Commander's ship *L'Orient*, and presented to His Lordship by his friend Captain Hollowell, after the Battle of the Nile, being then received on board, the leaden coffin was opened and the Body taken out; when it was found still in most excellent condition.

. . . This was the last time the mortal part of the lamented Hero was seen by human eyes; as the Body, after being dressed in a shirt, stockings, uniform small-clothes and waistcoat, neckcloth, and night-cap, was then placed in the shell made from the *L'Orient's* mast, and covered with the shrouding. This was inclosed in a leaden coffin; which was soldered up immediately, and put into another wooden shell: in which manner it was sent out of the *Victory* into Commissioner Grey's yacht, which was hauled alongside for that purpose. In this vessel the revered remains were conveyed to Greenwich Hospital.

During its journey round the Sussex and Kent coast before the transference of the body to the yacht, the *Victory* made a short stop at Broadstairs, where the leaguer containing the body could be seen from the shore. Fort House (later lived in by Dickens and subsequently renamed 'Bleak House') was at that time the house of the Commander of the North Cliff Battery, and the flags were lowered on fort and house as a mark of respect and forty-seven guns were fired, representing Nelson's age.

Nelson's body rested at Greenwich Hospital over Christmas 1805. In early January he lay in state in the Painted Hall at Greenwich for three days and an estimated 30,000 people paid their last respects. On Wednesday 8 January the body was escorted to the funeral barge by 500 naval pensioners. The barge and its crew were from the *Victory*, and the mourners were led by two of Nelson's former commanding officers, Admiral of Fleet Sir Peter Parker, and Admiral Lord Hood, the governor of the Royal Hospital at Greenwich.

Thousands of mourners lined the banks of the Thames to watch Nelson's body taken to the Admiralty in a procession of five barges. Four of the barges were covered in black cloth and, according to the official programme, the middle funeral barge was 'covered with Black Velvet, the Top adorned with Plumes of Black Feathers, and, in the Centre, upon Four Shields of the Arms of the Deceased, joining in point, a Viscount's Coronet'.

The next day, Nelson's funeral was held at St Paul's Cathedral. The official programme describes the mourners in procession:

Forty-eight Pensioners from Greenwich Hospital, Two and Two, in Mourning Cloaks, with Badges of the Crests of the Deceased on the Shoulders, and the Back Staves in their Hands.
Forty-eight Seamen of His Majesty's Ship THE VICTORY, Two and Two, in their Ordinary Dress, with Black Neck Handkerchiefs and Stockings, and Crepe in their hats.
Watermen of the Deceased in Black Coats, with their badges.
Officers, who attended the Body while it lay in State at Greenwich, in Mourning Coaches.

Extract from poem *Nelson's Tomb* by William Fitzgerald:

Behold! The VICTOR SHIP to port advance
With him, who crush'd the naval power of France;
With him, who triumphed with his latest breath,
And purchas'd fame immortal by his death.
THAT SHIP, which still his conquering standard bore,
Brings her dead Hero to Britannia's shore;
High on her mast the laurel branch is seen,
But cypress mingles with the deathless green . . .

The lying in state of Nelson at Greenwich Hospital

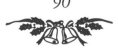

Strange Sightings at Christmastide in Kent

Kent has its fair share of ghouls and ghosties, spectral coaches racing through the night and phantom apparitions roaming the corridors of great houses. The moans of incarcerated nuns, the laughter of cruel seducers and the screams of unavenged victims have all been vouched for by generations of Kentish witnesses. Even today there are those who speak with relish of audible but invisible armies tramping through the Kent countryside and of the pathetic cries of murdered babies issuing from under floor boards. We make no claims regarding the veracity of the following list of seasonal apparitions in Kent . . . but there are those who would.

The ancient town of Rochester in East Kent is dominated by a massive keep built in the reign of Henry I. Close by stands the great twelfth-century cathedral and clustering around it the remains of some of its former monastic buildings, the ruined chapter house and the cloisters. Three ancient gates, Priors Gate, Deanery Gate and Chertsey's Gate give entrance into the High Street. This last gate appears as Jasper's Gate in Charles Dickens' last and unfinished work, *The Mystery of Edwin Drood.*

Anne Boleyn, attributed to Holbein

Nearby is the Corn Exchange from the front of which projects a huge clock on an ornamental bracket which became the 'moon faced clock' of Dickens', *The Uncommercial Traveller*. It is before this clock on Christmas Eve that the spectre of Charles Dickens, evidently reluctant to leave his beloved Kent in which he spent the happiest days of his life, is said to appear. At the last stroke of twelve, Dickens slowly takes a gold watch from out of his waistcoat pocket . . . and solemnly checks the time before dematerializing in the early morning air.

The south coast of Kent had a unique sighting of a ghost ship at Christmastime. The story began one hundred years ago when a cross-Channel paddle-steamer named the SS *Violet* was driven on to the Goodwin Sands during a violent winter snowstorm. The wintry seas were mountainous and all hands and passengers drowned. At the start of the Second World War, a man on duty on the East Goodwin lightship reported an old fashioned paddle-steamer in difficulties on the sands. The lifeboat raced out to investigate . . . but there was nothing to be seen, only snow capped waves.

The picturesque North Downs village of Kemsing on the Pilgrim's Way resounds to the sound of a horse's hooves every Christmas Eve when the spectre of a Norman knight, bent on the murder of Becket, primate of all England, rides up to the ancient church and dismounts before the door.

Hever Castle in West Kent, the beautiful one-time home of the wealthy American Astor family, can boast a royal ghost, Anne Boleyn, the second in Henry VIII's line of unfortunate wives. Hever was once the home of the Boleyn family and Anne's ghost is said to manifest itself each Christmas Eve when her spectre lingers for a few moments on the bridge which spans the moat. This lovely castle was owned by Anne's father Thomas Boleyn and it was here that Henry courted and, some say, made her sister pregnant before turning his amorous attentions to the unfortunate girl who would for such a brief period become queen of England and mother to Queen Elizabeth I.

Rainham in north Kent would have us believe that a phantom coach makes a regular spectral Christmas Eve appearance. This coach, driven by a headless coachman, pulled by headless horses and with a headless passenger inside, is said to leave the church at a rapid pace and, with only one very brief stop to water the headless horses, races to Bloor's Place where it turns into the grounds and promptly melts into the morning air. Until relatively recently, a glass of brandy was left out for the refreshment of the phantom traveller.

The superstitious will avoid a Christmas Eve visit to 'The

Mourning Tree' – a Canadian cypress growing in the churchyard of Bearsted village. Sited a little way along the Ashford Road out of Maidstone, for generations it was surrounded by cherry orchards and hop fields. This tree was planted by the vicar who used it to mark the grave of a nineteen-year-old boy, John Dyke, who had been publicly hanged on Peneden Heath on Christmas Eve 1830, accused of firing a rick. Tragically, only a few years after the hanging, a local man made a deathbed confession to the crime. When the body was interred, the coffin was deliberately set on the other side of the churchyard 'so that his presence shall not offend the innocent spirit of the scapegoat'.

When Thomas à Becket was brutally murdered in Canterbury Cathedral on the fourth day of Christmas, his body was laid on a bier before the high altar and his brains and blood collected and preserved separately. Later, drops of this blood were enclosed in tiny lead flasks which were sold as pilgrim's badges and which were reputed to have healing powers. The content of the flasks was known as 'Canterbury Water' and the containers were usually stamped with the words *Optimus egrorum medicus fit Thomas honorum*. In Canterbury itself the sainthood of the murdered prelate was soon made manifest to the citizens by the fact that the public well in Sun Street ran red with the saint's blood. A red and gold pump fixed high up a wall today marks the original site of the miraculous well.

from

A Window on a Hill – 'A Small Parcel'

RICHARD CHURCH

Richard Church (1893–1972) was a South Londoner who explored Kent by bicycle in his youth and then moved to the county in 1939 to live in a converted oasthouse at Curtisden Green, near Goudhurst. A Window on the Hill *is a collection of essays – many of them about country life in the Kentish Weald around Goudhurst. This particular extract deals with the arrival of the post boy with a seasonal parcel of goodies from abroad during the great freeze of the winter of 1946–7 when rationing was still in force.*

During the great freeze-up of 1947, there were some days when no human soul approached this isolated dwelling, and here we sat, a world unto ourselves, contriving by force of circumstances and by the spirit within us, to fit the hours of

snow-muffled solitude with all that tiny drama of ordinary doings and events which usually go unrecorded . . . .

I do not apologize, therefore, in describing a small happening that came to enliven a snowbound day in our hill-top oasthouse, where we live, normally, so vivid an existence amongst the cherry orchards and hop-gardens of Kent, some fifty miles from London geographically, but two hundred years away from it in terms of character and habit.

I say that the day was uneventful, but that is hardly a grateful statement, for out of doors a most astonishing miracle had taken place during the night. A sudden rise in temperature the previous day (a false pause in the seven-week frost) had led to storms of sleety rain, which had stuck to the trees and shrubs like toffee. During the night it froze, and we got up to find a world set in crystal, like expensive confectionery which one used to buy before the war. On the terrace looking south stands a large smooth-leaved holly tree. Every leaf that morning was a long lozenge of glass. And a weeping willow by the solid pond was now a system of rods of varying thickness. The deadly silence of absolute cold lay over the landscape. Suddenly a waft of air passed across the snow, beneath the dull, leaden sky. And to my ears there came a snow-maiden music, straight from the realm of Hans Andersen. It was the

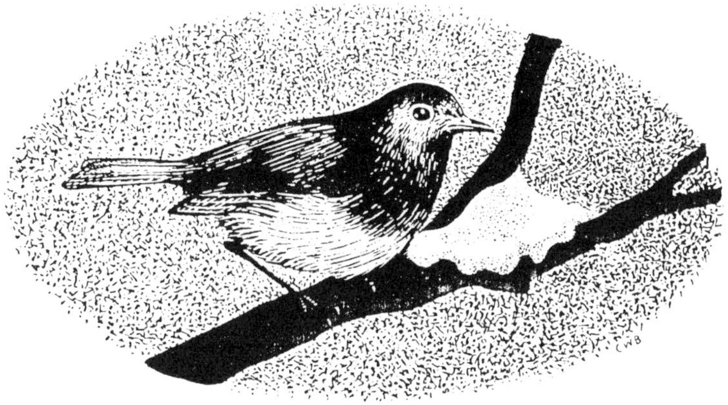

tinkling of the crystals of holly and willow, the rods and the lozenges clanging and rattling. I stood there, marvelling, and blaming myself for the depression which the intense cold and the post-war discomforts of a fuelless and almost foodless house had put upon my mind. Here was the very voice of joy itself, disembodied and gay, right in the midst of a mournful, adamantine universe of tomb-like rigidity.

But all that is by the way. The small incident of the day has yet to be recorded. It came about noon, in the shape of a small boy wrapped from head to feet in khaki woollens, the relics of family Home Guard garments. He was the auxiliary postman! This Disney-like little figure handed me no letters (for all business seemed to come to a standstill during those black days). He carried a parcel under his arm, while he prodded his way with a long walking-stick to make sure of his footing.

We brought him into the kitchen and gave him a cup of hot tea. He told us of the outside world, and hold-up of traffic on the roads and railway. Then he looked slyly at the parcel and said, 'Do you see that's come from America? I suppose you don't want to keep the stamps?' We assured him that our interest in stamps had been outgrown some forty years ago, and we carefully tore them off the parcel while he was consuming his tea. Off he went with his trophy, and left us alone once more, to examine, after an exciting speculation, the parcel.

The parcel! It contained all sorts of delights whose nature we had almost begun to forget: a packet of rice, dried bananas, really sweet chocolate, a tin of honey, another of peaches, yet another of hamburgers; even a packet of suet. The contents spread out on the table seemed to radiate warmth, concentrated sunlight. We looked at these samples of another world, and then we looked at each other. And we both knew what our thoughts were. They were a mutual appreciation of the miracle of friendship. For in the box was a slip of paper with the name and address of friends whom we had neither seen nor heard of for at least two years. But they had remembered us, and had taken the trouble to have this substantial message despatched from New York.

A Christmas Tradition of the Frittenden Band

ALAN AUSTEN

Alan Austen, morris man, mummer, folk-singer and member of the appropriately named 'Wassail Country Dance Band', is a fine example of someone living the traditional Kent life. He has revived the West Malling Mummers Play tradition in pubs in the village on the last Saturday before Christmas and regularly sings traditional Kent and Sussex songs, and some of his own compositions in the idiom, at Kent folk clubs. This is a story he heard during his researches of Kent traditional material, connected with the little village of Frittenden near Headcorn.

In days gone by Kent villages and towns would often have their own bands. In the tiny village of Frittenden, near Headcorn, the local pub, the Bell and Jorrocks, combines the names of the two local hostelries (the Bell having closed some years ago). The existing pub was originally called the John Jorrocks, named after the famous huntsman of that name celebrated in the book by Surtees *Jorrocks, Jaunts and Jollities*. It is still the focal point of Frittenden village life and is now the

'Them Frittenden Band Chaps.' A drawing made in 1926 from the 1860 photograph of the Frittenden Band

home pub of one of Kent's leading morris teams, the 'Mr Jorrocks'.

The Boxing Day hunt is still an important feature of Kent rural life in some areas, and the local hunt sometimes meets at The Bell and Jorrocks, but another link between this pub and Christmas festivities occurs through an old photograph of a band on the wall of the Saloon bar. This is of the celebrated Frittenden Band, taken in the year 1860 when the band made a celebrated trip to London, which is still the subject of local anecdotes.

In days gone by villages and towns often had their own bands, which would play at important times of the year, including Christmas. There were Kent versions of well known carols set to local tunes. For example, traditional singer Les Waghorn remembers singing the well known carol 'While Shepherds Watched' in Headcorn Chapel to a tune composed in Kent called 'Cranbrook' (and borrowed for the song 'Ilkley Moor Ba Tat').

The following story was told to me some years ago about an occasion when the Frittenden Band were touring round the neighbourhood at Christmas time playing carols to the outlying farms and houses:

That particular Christmas Eve was very foggy as is often the case in the low-lying areas of the Weald. The Band consisted of mainly brass instruments (even including a flugel horn), unlike the string-dominated quires of Wessex described by Thomas Hardy. The line-up of the team musicians was: bass drum, flugel horn, two cornets, French horn, trombone, uphonium, tuba and side-drum.

Although hardly being able to read the music in front of them, the musicians were not put off by the fog and set off in high spirits having fortified themselves with good Kentish ale at The Bell and Jorrocks. They moved round from house to house and from farm to farm playing their Christmas repertoire and receiving mince pies and hot cider punch.

The fog grew thicker and thicker and the musicians began to long for the roaring open fire of The Bell and Jorrocks. Around midnight they cautiously felt their way across the fields to their last port of call, an outlying farmhouse renowned for its hospitality and for that reason selected as the final visit. The shadowy outline of the old building seemed to loom through the mist as they played their carols. There they were in full swing, halfway through 'Hark the Herald Angels Sing', when all of a sudden, as if by magic, the fog lifted and to their surprise they found themselves playing – to a haystack!

'For God, King Charles and Kent' – The Plum Pottage Riots

The Puritans were opposed to the celebration of Christmas partly because of their general antipathy to 'Masses' as being superstitious. In particular they abhorred the conviviality of Christmas and the links of its symbolism and seasonal significance with earlier pagan beliefs. Once the Roundheads took control of Kent during the Civil War, there was inevitable friction over the attempts of Kentishmen to maintain their seasonal celebrations and church services. Loyalties in Canterbury were closely divided between king and parliament, though there was strong opposition to the damage done to the cathedral by the Puritans. In the later 1640s sympathy began to swing to the king's cause in Canterbury and Christmas clashes provided the spark which ignited a royalist rising in Kent.

In December 1647 the Puritan Mayor of Canterbury, William Bridge, proclaimed that by order of parliament, 'Christmas Days and all other superstitious festivals are utterly abolished.'

He announced that the usual Saturday market would be held on Christmas Day (which that year fell on a Saturday), that shops should open and that no church services were to be held. He warned that anyone who hung 'rosemary, holly, or bayes or other superstitious herbs' at his door or made 'either plum pottage or nativity pies' would be going against the orders of parliament.

On Christmas Day, in defiance of this proclamation, Mr Aldy, Minister of St Andrew's, preached in his church, but the local Puritans made noisy demonstrations outside the church to try to disturb the service. Only twelve shops opened and Royalists tried to persuade these to close by damaging the goods they had on sale. The mayor went about Canterbury encouraging the shopkeepers to open up and when one of them answered him rudely, the mayor struck him in the face and was himself seized and thrown into the gutter. This was followed by other assaults on Puritans; their windows broken

St George's Gate, Canterbury

and their goods thrown about the streets. The Royalists barricaded St George's Gate, Burgate and Wincheap Gate with timber and their watchword was 'For God, King Charles and Kent'.

On Boxing Day the mayor set a small armed guard to watch the gates. Their leader, a barber named White, shot one of the crowd for calling him a 'Roundhead', which caused a fresh riot. The citizens 'came forth with clubs', Captain White was assaulted and imprisoned, the mayor fled and his house was attacked. The rioters obtained the keys to the prison and set their own guard over the city. By 27 December the insurgents had increased to over a thousand in number and they took control of the Town Hall and with it a supply of arms and powder. When the sheriff intervened to try to rescue Captain White 'he was knocked down and his head fearfully broke; it was God's mercy his brains were not beat out.' Other puritans were attacked, including Thomas Harris who was described as 'a busy prating fellow'.

Eventually, the Justices of the Peace persuaded the citizens to lay down their arms, with a promise that no retribution would be taken against them. However, the mayor brought in three thousand Roundhead soldiers, who damaged the city gates and walls and imprisoned the Justices in Leeds Castle for two months. Some of the rioters were imprisoned and tried, including the poet Francis Lovelace, who wrote his poem *To Althea From Prison* on this occasion which has the famous line 'Stone walls do not a prison make'. The jury threw out all the charges and organized a petition asking that the king and parliament should settle 'the Peace both of Church and Commonwealth'. Parliament's reaction to this was a threat to hang two petitioners from each parish and this led to a general Royalist uprising in Kent, defeated in a pitched battle at Maidstone.

Not until the Restoration of Charles II, the 'Merry Monarch' was Christmas properly celebrated again in Kent with church services, evergreen decorations, singing and dancing and seasonal food and drink. Appropriately Charles landed in Kent on his return from exile and progressed through the county to London.

Christmas Presents

FRANK KENDON

This extract from Frank Kendon's exquisite chapter 'Christmas Day' in his book The Small Years *vividly re-creates both the magical and practical importance of presents in childhood. Unusually, it dwells on children's excitement from marshalling their small resources to buy presents for others in a shopping expedition to Goudhurst.*

Frank Kendon (1893–1969) is well known as a publisher, poet and novelist. The Small Years *describes his boyhood at his family's school at Winchet Hill near Horsmonden in the Kentish Weald.*

Christmas was the natural climax of any year. For John and me, for Stella and Carrie and those of the small fry who had any power at all over time, there were two such days and no more in every year – birthday, and Christmas Day. These had the closest association in our minds, though the only factor common to both was this receiving of presents. Nobody under

fourteen had any doubt about the matter. It was not greed. We depended for our possessions entirely upon gifts, and chiefly upon what fell to our lot on these two generous days.

The penny that came on Saturday was improvidently spent on Saturday; and even so simple a necessity as a pocket-knife was beyond hope of purchase. Thus, also, with pencils and rubbers, rich crayons and paints, drums, whips, hoops, printing outfits, pistols, autograph albums, telescopes, compasses, snakes-and-ladders, balls, carpentry sets (to speak only in a masculine way) and suchlike necessities. We were bound to be dependent upon presents; an unfortunate Christmas meant an ill-equipped life; it meant borrowed paints, hunting for someone to sharpen a pencil, handicaps.

. . . Christmas was, in the manner of gifts, everybody's birthday. Aunts one merely noticed in May both generously gave and rightly received presents at Christmas time; and no-one wished to shirk responsibilities . . . Even at six a child could, and would, fold pointed paper 'hair-tidies' or spills, or blanket-stitch a kettleholder. At the least everyone could, and many did, paint easy plum puddings and holly for cards for the last remembered. There was a fever of work and secrecy in those last days, until the afternoon before Christmas, when blessed with permissive weather, we got together the pence we had come by, and an extra sixpence or so from relenting parents, and we set out to walk the two miles through the winter lanes over the hills to shop at Goudhurst.

Miss Button's shop was . . . a small triangular room, with the door (automatically ringing a shaker bell as you entered) at the pointed end . . . Do you know those limp, canvas-bodied dolls, with shiny china-ware heads and necks, no clothes, but pointed black, glossy, heavy cold clicking French boots on the leg-ends? Miss Button had boxes of them. She had packs of parlour games, Snap, Happy Families, Ludo, crisp Dominoes, rattling Halmas and, of course, such things as marbles (in tape-tied bags), lead soldiers, pop-guns, and wooden symbols of engines and horses so hardened in convention by an ancient ritual of toymaking that they bore no more resemblance to real trains and horses than the pegged knees and hips and flat bellies of wooden Dutch dolls bore to our own well-known anatomies. But the smell, and then the touch, of the newness was everywhere, and though drums and musical boxes were, as Miss Button knew, for ever out of reach of our purses, we might linger over them, see how they worked, enjoy them in all but the having. When at last we set out on the long walk home, easily carrying our parcels, we knew that the last turnstile had been passed. No more presents could be bought, no more now could even be finished off. It was supper and bed as soon as we had labelled the last of our packets and told our mother all over the cocoa. Carol singers faltered in the dark below us while we undressed and said our prayers.

from

Bygone Kent – 'Royal Christmases at Eltham'

JIM LANDERGAN

Eltham was formerly in Kent, but has now been swallowed up by Greater London. Eltham Palace dates from the thirteenth century, but was largely rebuilt from the fifteenth century onwards. The late fifteenth-century hall with its fine hammer-beam roof, the site of the Christmas festivities, still survives and is in the care of English Heritage.

Eltham Palace was one of the favourite royal residences from the fourteenth century to the time of the Tudors. Many monarchs, from Richard II to Henry VIII spent Christmas there and detailed records survive. This article presents a vivid selection of medieval and Tudor royal Christmases at Eltham and includes information on the food and entertainment.

As Christmas nears, houses throughout the land mark its

coming with colourful decorations, evergreen garlands and tinsel-decked trees with twinkling multi-coloured lights. They will be seen in the homes around the site that was once Eltham Palace, where staid and sombre, the Great Hall, the only building of the royal palace still to stand, silently reminds us of the many regal Christmases spent within the palace walls in Plantagenet and Tudor times.

Anthony Bek, Bishop of Durham, built the palace and in 1305 presented it to Isabella, wife of the Prince of Wales – later Edward II. But even before the palace was built there had been a royal visitor at Eltham for the festive season. Matthew Paris, the chronicler-monk of St Albans, tells how in 1270 'King Henry III kept a mighty Christmas here according to the customs of those times, being accompanied by the Queen and all of the nobility.'

For nearly three hundred years Eltham Palace was a favourite residence of many kings, from Edward II to Henry VIII, and numerous royal gatherings at Christmas saw great feasting with much merry-making, music, masques and mumming, as well as diplomatic missions by foreign potentates, affairs of state, and murder plots against the lives of kings. There was legend, too.

Richard II, with his wife Anne of Bohemia, was the first reigning monarch to spend Christmas at Eltham Palace, in 1384. The festivities were on a magnificent scale, for Richard entertained more lavishly than any previous king. Holinshed in his *Chronicles* writes of Richard, '. . . he maintained the most plentiful house that ever any king in England did, either before his day or since, for there resorted daily to his court above ten thousand persons that had meat and drink allowed them. In his kitchen there were three hundred servitors, and every other office was furnished after the like rate; of ladies, chamberers, and larderers there were above three hundred at the least, and in precious and costly apparel they exceeded all

Eltham Palace: the great hall

measure. Yeomen and grooms were clothed in silks, with cloth of graine and scarlet, oversumptuous ye may be sure for their style.'

The royal couple returned for Christmas 1385 and again in 1386 when they had an unexpected guest, Leo, King of Armenia. The Armenian came uninvited, ostensibly to mediate between the kings of France and England. Whatever the real purpose of King Leo's visit he was entertained munificently, presented with many costly gifts, and granted a royal charter of £1,000 a year for life.

Christmas 1400 saw a similar imperial visit to Eltham when Henry IV regaled the Byzantine Emperor, Manuel II, who came to plead for assistance against Bajazet, Emperor of the Turks, who had sacked Constantinople. Manuel II received a grant of £2,000 from the Exchequer towards the relief of the city.

Henry IV resided much of his time at Eltham where he spent ten of the fourteen Christmases of his reign. In 1404 a plot to kill him was discovered just hours before it was due to happen. Holinshed tells of the plan, '. . . the Duke of York was meant to have broken into the Manor of Eltham the last Christmas by scaling the walls in the night season, the King being there the same season, to the intent to have murdered him.' The duke was arrested, imprisoned in the Tower, but freed without trial some months later.

The king and his court were at Eltham again for Christmas 1405 and they returned to celebrate the festival there five times in the succeeding six years.

Henry IV's last Christmas in 1412 was a sad occasion. Throughout, the king lay in his chamber at Eltham Palace. Tended by the queen, the bedridden monarch lay still, without speaking, without moving, his face disfigured by a virulent skin disease, at times it seemed that he was dead. Rallying a little as the festive season ended he was carried to Westminster where, shortly after, he died.

His son, Henry V, spent much of his nine-year reign engaged in his consuming passion, the conquest of France. He kept only one Christmas at Eltham, the first of his reign in 1413, but the festivities came to a sudden end when the king learned of a conspiracy by Sir Roger Acton and Lord Cobham to murder him. The king's spy, Thomas Burton, was paid £5 for watching the Lollards and informing Henry of the plan. Acton and twenty-eight others were accused and condemned. They were drawn, hanged, and their bodies burned.

Henry VI was born in 1421, only nine months before the death of his father Henry V. His childhood Christmases were spent at Eltham but little is known of them. Bands of strolling players, jugglers, jesters and minstrels, were brought to court to amuse the child monarch and in 1426 his gifts included coral beads that had belonged to his great-great-grandfather,

Edward III. Henry VI was at Eltham for Christmas 1429 when he was eight years old, but he did not spend another there.

In 1454 Edward IV took his newly-wed queen, Elizabeth Woodville, to Eltham Palace for Christmas, commanding the Exchequer to pay 'to our right entirely well beloved wife the Queen, for the expenses of her chamber, wardrobe and stable, against this feast of Christmas coming, £466 13s. 4d.'

Edward IV's Christmas at Eltham in 1482 reflected the character of the man and the prosperity of the country. In the *Chronicles of Croyland* John Russell, Bishop of Lincoln and Lord Chancellor to Richard III, writes of the clothes Edward wore for the festive season, '. . . clad in a great variety of most costly garments, of quite different cut from those which had hitherto been seen in our country.' And the foods supplied for the 2,000 guests for the twelve days of Christmas were listed:

Sheep	1,000	Calves	300	Pigs	800
Swans	2,000	Geese	1,000	Capons	2,000
Bulls	6	Plovers	1,200	Quails	2,400
Peacocks	400	Cranes	200	Kids	2,000
Bitterns	4,000	Heronshaws	200	Curlews	1,000
Dishes of jelly	4,000	Hot custards	2,000	Porpoises & Seals	12
Cold venison pastries	1,000	Hot venison pastries	15,000		

Spices, Sugared Delicacies, and Wafers – plenty.

As a child the young Prince Henry lived and was educated at Eltham, but it was not until 1515, the the sixth year of his reign, that Henry VIII and his court were at Eltham Palace for Christmas. The occasion was splendid and regal, but matters of state were attended to as well. After vespers on Christmas Eve, in the chapel built by Henry, Cardinal Wolsey took the oath of office as Lord Chancellor of England.

At the traditional banquet on Christmas Day the boar's

head, heralded by a trumpet fanfare, was carried into the hall head high on a gold salver while the choir sang:

> The boar's head in hand bring I,
> With garland gay and rosemary,
> I pray you all sing merrily,
> Qui estis in convivio!

In the days following the festivities continued, jousting and hunting by day, feasting and merry-making by night, culminating on Twelfth Night with a performance in the afternoon of 'Troilus and Pandarus' by the children of the chapel. Records show that the barber was paid fourpence for washing and cutting the hair of the fifteen young performers.

In the evening a grand masque was acted out. A castle constructed within the hall, defended by a group of nobles and their ladies was attacked by other knights. A fierce mock battle ensued, the defendants triumphed and came out to join their assailants in stately dance. Afterwards a banquet with two hundred dishes was served to all.

Henry VIII came again to Eltham for Christmas 1525. A plague was raging in London: Greenwich, by now the king's favourite residence, was a suspect area, so Henry, and his court, came to the quiet, healthy air of his Kentish palace. The Lord Chancellor came too and whilst there drew up the *Statutes of Eltham*, rules for the manner and conduct of the royal household. They give an interesting insight into the conduct of a noble house of the period.

'Master cooks', the rules stipulated, 'Shall employ such scullions as shall not go naked, nor lie about all night before the kitchen fire.' Full use was to be made of the hours of daylight, 'dinner shall be at ten, supper at four.' Wholemeal bread was not prized, 'of bread made of wheat we have sundrie sorts dailie brought to the table whereof the first and most excellent is the manchet which we commonly call white bread.'

The *Statutes* set down scales of hospitality. A duke or an archbishop was allowed stabling for twenty-four horses and beds for nine servants; those of lower degree had stabling for only two horses and beds for two servants. In the morning a duke would receive one chett loaf, one manchet, one gallon of ale; at midday, one manchet, one gallon of ale; in the afternoon, one chett loaf, one manchet, one gallon of ale, one pitcher of wine and a good supply of coals, candles and torches. Lowest on the list, the queen's laundress was provided only with coals, candles and twopence a day for board wages.

There is a legend that Anne Boleyn was a guest at Eltham Palace that Christmas and was the central figure of an ominous happening there. Anne was eighteen, recently returned from France where she was educated. Henry had tired of her elder sister, Mary, as his mistress: attracted by the sight of the almond-shaped eyes, the raven-black hair and the vivacious manner of the young Anne Boleyn he invited her to join the royal party for Christmas.

At the grand feast on Christmas Day the boar's head was borne in with traditional ceremony. There followed the dish considered more suitable and delicate to the female palate, roast peacock. The bird was carefully skinned so that the plumage, undamaged remained attached, and prepared for the oven. Stuffed with spices and sweet herbs it was basted during the roasting with the yolks of hens' eggs. When cooked it stood to cool, then, beak gilded and body decorated with Henry's arms in gold leaf, was carried by the most distinguished or most beautiful lady present, escorted by the other lady guests, and set before the king.

The honour, so the legend runs, was given to Anne, but as she put down the dish on the table the peacock's head fell. The merry chatter around the hall was stilled, for a moment all was quiet, then a murmur rose but as it grew suddenly above it all one voice was heard, 'An omen, alas poor Anne Boleyn, an omen that one day her head will fall as well!'

There never was another royal Christmas at Eltham. Visits by reigning monarch became fewer and with the Stuarts stopped. For more than four hundred and fifty years, since Henry VIII no English king has stayed in Eltham for Christmas, but maybe every year on that December night, when all is quiet and no one stirs, the shades of long-dead kings and queens with silk-clad courtiers emerge to continue their festive revels.

Twelfth Cake

Twelfth Night (6 January) marked the end of the traditional celebration of the Twelve Days of Christmas. The climax was often in the form of a party in which a special Twelfth Cake was eaten. Cooked into the cake would be a pea and a bean and whoever found these in their portion was crowned king and queen.

This recipe comes from Rochester and was collected by former reference librarian and local history consultant, Catherine Rothwell.

1 lb butter
1 lb castor sugar
8 eggs (yolks and white separated)

4 oz blanched almonds
2 wine glasses brandy
1 lb flour
½ lb mixed peel
3 lb currants

Beat the butter and sugar to a fluffy cream. Add the eggs very gradually. The currants, peel and almonds meanwhile should be marinading in the brandy. Mix the flour gradually, then all the rest. A large, well-greased tin lined with several thicknesses of greaseproof paper is necessary for the mixture, which should be baked at 160°C/325°F/Gas Mark 3 for at least 4 hours. Test with a thin skewer and if it comes out clean remove from the oven and allow to stand for 35 minutes before turning out of the tin.

I found that this rich plum cake was most successful with the oven to itself, in splendid isolation, left undisturbed for the time quoted.

'The Prioress's Tale'

GEOFFREY CHAUCER

Often called the 'Father of English Poetry', Geoffrey Chaucer, a fourteenth-century courtier – poet, ultimately made his home in Kent. In 1385 he was made a justice of the peace and sat in parliament as knight of the shire for that county.

The Canterbury Tales *is undoubtedly his most popular work, and it deals with a band of pilgrims heading for the shrine of St Thomas à Becket in Canterbury, telling stories as they go. One of the pilgrims is a Prioress and she tells the story of the martyrdom of a little choirboy who, having been horribly murdered, is stuffed down a privy. As his mother feverishly seeks for him the child makes his presence miraculously known by singing an anthem in honour of the Virgin which he had been learning for Christmas.*

This extract from the 'Prioress's Tale' by Geoffrey Chaucer is translated by Fran Doel.

This poor widow waited all that night
for her little child, but he did not come;
and so, as soon as it was daylight,
with the pale face of dread and distraught mind,
she sought for him at school and elsewhere,
until finally she got so far as to discern
that he was last seen in the ghetto . . . .

She asked and begged piteously
to each one that lived in that place
to tell her if her child had gone by at all.
They said no, but Jesus, of his grace
put it into her mind after a short time
to call out for her son in that place
next to which he had been cast in a pit.

O mighty God, whose praise is made manifest
by the mouths of innocents, behold here they might!
This gem of chastity, this emerald,

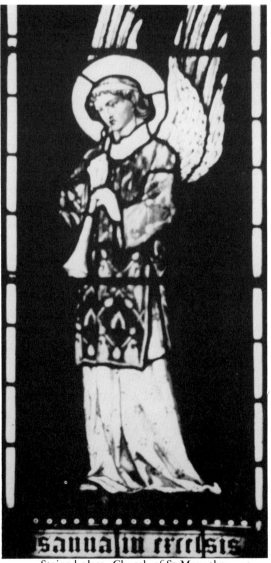

Stained glass, Church of St Mary the Virgin, Speldhurst

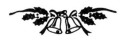

this bright ruby of martyrdom,
there as he lay, face uppermost with his throat cut,
he began to sing Alma redemptoris
so loudly that the whole place rang with the sound.

The Christian folk who were going through the street
came in to marvel at this thing,
and they hastily sent for the provost;
he came at once without tarrying
and praised Christ who is king of heaven,
and his mother as well, honour of mankind;
and after that he had the culprits bound.

The child was taken up with piteous lamentation,
continually singing his song,
and with full processional honour,
they carried him to the nearest abbey.
His mother lay swooning by the bier;
(the people could scarcely
remove this latter-day Rachel from it).

With torments and with shameful death
this provost at once put each one that
knew of this murder to death;
he would not countenance such cursedness.
Evil shall get its deserts,
therefore he had them drawn with wild horses,
and after that he hanged them according to law.

This innocent still lay on his bier
before the high altar, while mass lasted,
and after that the abbot with his convent
made haste to have him buried.
But even though they sprinkled holy water over him,
the child still sang
O Alma redemptoris mater when asperged.

The abbot who was a holy man
as monks are (or at least should be)
began to entreat this young child,
and said 'O dear child, I beseech thee,
by virtue of the Holy Trinity,
tell me what enables you to sing
for your throat has been cut as far as I can see.'

'My throat is cut through to the neck bone,'
said this child, 'and, according to the laws of nature
I should have died a long time ago;
but Jesus Christ (as you will find in books)
wants his glory to endure and to be kept in mind;
and so that his dear mother be honoured
permits me to sing O Alma loud and clear.

I always loved Christ's sweet mother
this well of mercy, as best I could;
and when I was about to lose my life
she came to me and told me to sing
this anthem as I died.
As you have heard, and when I had sung,
it seemed to me she put a grain upon my tongue.

Therefore I sing, and must go on singing
in honour of this blissful maiden,
until the grain is removed from under my tongue;
and afterwards she said to me,
"My little child, I will come to fetch you
when the grain is taken from under your tongue;
do not be afraid, I will not forsake you."'

This holy monk, this abbot of whom I spoke,
pulled out the tongue and took away the grain,
and quietly the child gave up the ghost.
When the abbot had seen this miracle,

salt tears trickled down his cheeks like rain,
and he fell prone upon the ground
and lay as still as if he had been bound.

The rest of the convent also prostrated themselves,
weeping and praising Christ's dear mother,
and after that they rose and went forth,
taking the martyr from his bier,
and they enclosed his sweet little body
in a tomb of shining marble,
where he is to this day (God grant that we may meet).

The Darent Valley Champions

SIMON EVANS

Despite assertions by scholars that Kent has no mummers' plays, there is a strong tradition in the north and west of the county. A fine play was collected from the village of Bearsted in the nineteenth century and is regularly performed in venues in West Kent by the Tonbridge Mummers each Christmas. Alan Austen has revived the West Malling play, which can be seen in the pubs there on the last Saturday before Christmas. But the strongest tradition, described in this article, comes from the Darent Valley, where several plays have been collected.

Simon Evans is a writer and broadcaster on the folk arts and a musician and dancer with the Hartley Morris Men and White Star Sword Dancers. A resident of North Kent, he continues to research local folk customs and takes a keen interest in their revival and perpetuation. During the 1970s he collaborated with fellow musician and broadcaster Charlie Jacobs in researching the Darent Valley Mummer's plays and these two have taken a leading role in the revival of the plays.

The River Darent rises in the hills above Westerham and winds its way through some of the most beautiful countryside in North Kent, before cutting its way through urban Dartford and flowing on into the Thames.

Every Christmas in the villages that lay along the river, an ancient drama was acted out by groups of players who travelled many miles on foot through dark lanes and woods to bring their Yuletide ritual to every part of the valley. In all, there were four teams – based in the villages of Brasted, Riverhead, Shoreham and Sutton-at-Hone – each with a different version of the play and each with its own territory, performing in their own and neighbouring villages as well as in the surrounding hamlets and farmhouses. Generations of working people had maintained the guardianship of these plays, never needing to question the origins or the reasons for keeping up the custom. The tradition was a part of village life for as long as anyone could remember and Christmas simply wouldn't have been Christmas without it.

These Darent Valley groups of mummers were known as the 'Christmas Champions' and their season began in mid-December, when they would take in all the large households, performing for the gentry and their staff. Hallways and

The Tonbridge Mummers outside the Rose and Crown Hotel, Tonbridge, Boxing Day 1989

kitchens rattled to the sound of wooden swords on shields as the well-to-do tolerated the upholding of this old custom, before sending the players on their way with a drink and a contribution in the hat. The Champions walked for miles to visit each house in turn. Lords and ladies, businessmen and bankers, all witnessed the spectacle of half a dozen men with blackened faces, covered all over with strips of paper, reciting ten minutes of doggerel in which King George slew the Turkish Knight, before being deftly revived by a boastful quack Doctor. Finally, a few days before Christmas, the Champions turned their attention to the pubs in the surrounding area, before concluding the season with a Christmas Eve tour of their own village pubs.

At one time many villages in England had a team of mummers, each with their own version of the play, and in spite of the differences between them the central theme is nearly always the same, the 'baddie' is killed and then brought back to life by the mysterious Doctor. There is no doubt that the tradition is very old, perhaps going back to the time when the shortest days and turning of the year were celebrated by the festival of Yule. The symbolic acting out of death and resurrection represents the renewal of life that gradually gets under way until springtime, when the living earth finally turns its back on the cold, dormant winter months.

There were usually six or seven players in each team in the Darent Valley, and upon arriving at a venue they would wait outside for their turn to enter. Father Christmas went first, bursting in unannounced:

In comes I, Old Father Christmas, am I welcome or am I not?
I hope Old Father Christmas will never be forgot.
For in this room there shall be shown
The dreadfullest battle ever known.
Step in King George with thy free heart
To see if thou canst claim peace in thine own part.

The rest of the players remained outside and out of sight, even though everybody knew they were there. The elements of surprise and anonymity were considered important. King George entered next, brandishing sword and spear and cursing the Turkish Knight, who upon hearing these oaths, would be the next in through the door to defend his reputation:

In comes I, Little Turkish Knight.
I comes from Turkish land to fight.
I'll fight with thee, King George, that man of courage bold,
If your blood be hot, I'll quickly fetch it cold.

In the ensuing combat the Turkish Knight fell to the ground, fatally wounded, with King George's sword under his armpit. The Doctor would be summoned and amid much hocus pocus and quackery, would administer the life-giving antidote which succeeded in resurrecting the Turkish Knight.

The final character to enter would be Little Johnny Jack 'with my wife and family on my back'. It would be his job to make the appeal for generosity before the hat was taken round, and pointing to a collection of dolls slung over his shoulder he would announce that:

My family is large and I am small
So every little bit helps us all.

It is probably this last part of the play which was responsible for its survival. Acute poverty existed among many rural working people and the extra funds that were realized by performing the play were an important addition to the Christmas budget. It was this, rather than any romantic notion of upholding tradition, that led to the perpetuation of the play into this century. In Brasted there were brushes with the law when the local policeman tried to stop the play on the grounds that the Champions were merely begging. It was only through the efforts of the local curate, the Revd Wheatley, who persuaded the authorities that it really was an old custom, that it was allowed to continue.

The Darent Valley Champions performing at Brasted, Christmas 1989

When war was declared in 1914, many of our ancient customs and practices which had struggled into the twentieth century finally succumbed. Ever since the industrial revolution the way of life in the countryside had been gradually changing and when the young men who performed the plays went away to war, the tradition ceased. Many of them never returned and those who did found themselves in a world that was to change so fast that the old ways were soon to be left behind. In the twenties and thirties there was an occasional revival, but to the players it never felt quite the same. The thread had been cut, the continuity with the past was broken. We were entering a period of mass entertainment, when the cinema, the radio and the gramaphone were soon to oust the old ways of making your own fun.

But in the mid-1970s after extensive research, the Christmas Champions were once again seen in the Valley. Every Christmas-time since then (usually in the week immediately before Christmas itself), the village pubs in Westerham, Brasted, Shoreham and Sutton-at-Hone have again been filled with the sounds of battle, the outrageous claims of the Doctor and the goodwill of Father Christmas and Johnny Jack. Perhaps the magic of the Doctor has been strong enough to last through the long hibernation, eventually to revive the play itself.

The Churchills' Christmases at Chartwell

Sir Winston Churchill bought Chartwell, on the Greensand Ridge near Westerham, in 1922. At that stage it was, in the main, a Victorian mansion made by enlarging an earlier farmhouse, its name coming from a well on the site. Churchill was captivated by the magnificent view across the Weald and its position only twenty-five miles from Wesstminster was very convenient. He employed the architect Philip Tilden to transform the building into a comfortable, but graceful family home, still retaining the central portions of the old Kentish farmhouse, part of which was used for Churchill's beamed study.

The Churchill family moved into Chartwell in 1924. Churchill's son Randolph was thirteen and his daughters Diana, Sarah and Mary were fifteen, ten and two respectively. It proved a very happy family home for over forty years – as Baroness Spencer-Churchill wrote in the Foreword to the National Trust guidebook (1968):

> My husband and I lived at Chartwell for over forty years. The written word cannot describe all that it meant to us and our children who grew up there.

Those forty years spanned Churchill's terms in office as Chancellor of the Exchequer and as Prime Minister, as well as his ten years out of office from 1929 when he kept in touch with the worsening situation in Europe. Much of his painting and writing was done at Chartwell and he helped to landscape the garden and tackled the bricklaying of cottages and garden walls.

The National Trust now preserves Chartwell and its grounds as a memorial to Sir Winston Churchill and Baroness Spencer-Churchill and there are still records and local memories of the wonderful family Christmases of the Churchills in the 1920s and 1930s.

The celebrations began on Christmas Eve when the choir from nearby Westerham Church sang for the Churchill family on the terrace at Chartwell and were thanked in an appropriately hospitable manner. The house was decorated with holly, ivy and other evergreens and a large Christmas tree was placed in the library and illuminated with a hundred white was candles. Under this tree Sir Winston and other members of

Chartwell under snow

the family, would give Christmas presents to the staff and thank them for their work during the year. Apparently one year the Christmas tree caught fire and Randolph Churchill fetched a fire extinguisher and put out the blaze.

In the late 1920s and early 1930s there was usually a good gathering of youngsters at Chartwell to celebrate Christmas. Locals remember children skating on the frozen lake and on one occasion an igloo being built. Baroness Spencer-Churchill has described in letters how, as indoor amusement, she and her daughters acted in family theatricals.

Chartwell was closed during the Second World War, though Churchill did contrive occasional visits to a cottage in the grounds. After the war, when Sir Winston was Leader of the Opposition and then Prime Minister for a second time, Chartwell again became a centre for cultural and social activity.

New Year Gifts At Court

The giving of gifts at the mid-winter period can be traced back to pagan times. The Roman practice, for example, included the giving of gifts both at the Saturnalia (which roughly corresponded in the calendar to our Christmas) and at the Kalends of January (the Roman New Year festival). The presents at the Saturnalia were particularly from wealthy families to their less fortunate neighbours, while at New Year presents were given to members of the same household, including children, servants and friends.

The records surviving in England, which are naturally mainly of the upper classes, show that in medieval, Tudor and Jacobean England, the giving of New Year gifts was far more prevalent than the giving of Christmas gifts.

The medieval monarchs and aristocrats gave gifts, sometimes of money, to their retainers at New Year or Christmas. Thus in December 1367, Geoffrey Chaucer, then a page in the household of Elizabeth, Countess of Ulster (wife of Prince Lionel), was given twenty shillings 'for necessaries at Christmas'. His wife, Phillipa, who was in service with John of Gaunt (and whose sister later married him), was given a New Year's gift of a silver-gilt buttoner with six buttons in 1373. She received silver-gilt cups for New Year's gifts in 1380–2.

In the sixteenth and early seventeenth centuries it was

Hever Castle, childhood home of Anne Boleyn

Penshurst Place, home of Sir Philip Sydney

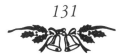

customary for the monarch to exchange New Year's gifts with his or her family and leading subjects. The following are some examples involving celebrities from the leading Kent country houses of Hever, Penshurst and Knole.

In 1532 Anne Boleyn, whose family seat was at Hever Castle, and whose mother and elder sister are said to have been Henry's mistresses before she married him, gave Henry VIII an exotic set of richly decorated Pyrenean boar spears. Henry gave Anne a matching set of hangings for her room and bed in cloth-of-gold, cloth-of-silver and richly embroidered crimson satin.

On New Year's Day, 1578, Sir Philip Sidney of Penshurst Place, the celebrated Kent poet, statesman and soldier, was at Court and presented Queen Elizabeth with 'a cambric chemise, wrought with black work, and a pair of ruffs set with spangles'. The Queen gave Sir Philip 'some gilt plate, weighing twenty-two ounces'.

Sir Philip then fell out of favour through opposing a projected marriage alliance between Queen Elizabeth and the Duc d'Anjou. His New Year's Day gifts to the queen in 1581 were thus highly symbolic – 'a whip to show that he had been scourged, a chain, to chain him to Her Majesty, and a heart of gold, to show that he was now entirely hers'. It may be on this occasion that Queen Elizabeth presented Sir Philip with the portrait of herself by Zucchero, which is still at Penshurst Place in Kent.

Lady Anne Clifford was countess in succession of Dorset, Pembroke and Montgomery and her diary survives for part of the time she lived at the delightful Elizabethan mansion, Knole House, in Knole Park near Sevenoaks. She was on close terms with James I's Queen Anne of Denmark and on New Year's Day 1616 she sent the queen a 'sweet bag'. In 1619 Lady Anne Clifford gave Queen Anne 'A New Year's gift, a cloth-of-silver cushion embroidered richly with the King of Denmark's arms, and all one with stripes of tent stitch.'

from

Pickwick Papers – 'Mr Pickwick on the Ice'

CHARLES DICKENS

Christmas Day in early nineteenth- century England was celebrated in a quiet way, with church in the morning followed by a special Christmas dinner in the afternoon. By contrast, the day that followed, Boxing Day, was a day of activity – and weather permitting, hunting, shooting, tobogganing, skating or snowballing might be the order of the day. This was also the day on which tradesmen and servants were traditionally offered gratuities and largesse dispensed to the poor.

In this episode of Pickwick Papers *the house party at Dingley Dell take to the ice with disastrous results for Mr Pickwick and Mr Winkle and Sam Weller is promised a well deserved Christmas box. Although Cob Tree Hall (the model for Manor Farm) has gone, the lake into which Mr Pickwick fell when he formed one of the skating party, can still be seen in the park.*

Old Wardle led the way to a pretty large sheet of ice; and the fat boy and Mr Weller, having shovelled and swept away the snow which had fallen on it during the night, Mr Bob Sawyer adjusted his skates with a dexterity which to Mr Winkle was perfectly marvellous and described circles with his left leg, and cut figures of eight, and inscribed upon the ice, without once stopping for breath, a great many other pleasant and astonishing devices, to the excessive satisfaction of Mr Pickwick, Mr Tupman, and the ladies: which reached a pitch of positive enthusiasm, when old Wardle and Benjamin Allen, assisted by the aforesaid Bob Sawyer, performed some mystic evolutions, which they called a reel.

All this time, Mr Winkle, with his face and hands blue with the cold had been forcing a gimlet into the soles of his feet, and putting his skates on, with the points behind, and getting the straps into a very complicated and entangled state, with the assistance of Mr Snodgrass who knew rather less about skates than a Hindoo. At length, however, with the assistance of Mr Weller the unfortunate skates were firmly screwed and buckled on, and Mr Winkle was raised to his feet.

'Now, then sir,' said Sam, in an encouraging tone; 'off with you, and show 'em how to do it.'

'Stop, Sam, stop!' said Mr Winkle, trembling violently. and clutching hold of Sam's arms with the grasp of a drowning man. 'How slippery it is, Sam.'

'Not an uncommon thing upon ice, sir,' replied Mr Weller. 'Hold up sir!'

This last observation of Mr Weller's bore reference to a demonstration Mr Winkle made at the instant, of a frantic desire to throw his feet in the air, and dash the back of his head on the ice.

'These – these – are very awkward skates; ain't they, Sam?' inquired Mr Winkle, staggering.

'I'm afeerd there's a orkard gem'lm'n in 'em sir,' replied Sam.

'Now, Winkle,' cried Mr Pickwick, quite unconscious that there was anything the matter. 'Come; the ladies are all anxiety.'

'Yes, yes,' replied Mr Winkle, with a ghastly smile. 'I'm coming.'

'Just a goin' to begin' said Sam, endeavouring to disengage himself. 'Now, sir, start off!'

'Stop an instant, Sam,' gasped Mr Winkle, clinging most affectionately to Mr Weller. 'I find I've got a couple of coats at home that I don't want, Sam. You may have them, Sam.'

'Thank'ee sir,' replied Mr Weller.

'Never mind touching your hat, Sam,' said Mr Winkle, hastily 'You needn't take your hand away to do that. I meant to have given you five shillings this morning for a Christmas-box, Sam. I'll give it you this afternoon, Sam.'

'You're very good, sir,' replied Mr Weller.

'Just hold me at first, Sam; will you?' said Mr Winkle. 'there – that's right. I shall soon get in the way of it, Sam. Not too fast, Sam; not too fast.'

Mr Winkle stooping forward, with his body half doubled up, was being assisted over the ice by Mr Weller, in a most singular and un-swan-like manner, when Mr Pickwick most innocently shouted from the opposite bank:

'Sam!'

'Sir?'

'Here. I want you.'

'Let go, sir,' said Sam. 'don't you hear the governor a callin? Let go, sir.'

With a violent effort, Mr Weller disengaged himself from the grasp of the agonised Pickwickian, and, in so doing, administered a considerable impetus to the unhappy Mr Winkle. With an accuracy which no degree of dexterity or

Mr Pickwick slides

practice could have insured, that unfortunate gentleman bore swiftly down into the centre of the reel, at the very moment when Mr Bob Sawyer was performing a flourish of unparalleled beauty. Mr Winkle struck wildly against him, and with a loud crash they both fell heavily down. Mr Pickwick ran to the spot. Bob Sawyer had risen to his feet, but Mr Winkle was far too wise to do anything of the kind in skates. He was seated on the ice, making spasmodic efforts to smile; but anguish was depicted on every lineament of his countenance.

'Are you hurt?' inquired Mr Benjamin Allen, with great anxiety.

'Not much,' said Mr Winkle, rubbing his back very hard.

'I wish you'd let me bleed you,' said Mr Benjamin, with great eagerness.

'No, thank you,' replied Mr Winkle hurriedly.

'I really think you had better,' said Allen.

'Thank you,' replied Mr Winkle; 'I'd rather not.'

'What do *you* think, Mr Pickwick?' inquired Bob Sawyer.

Mr Pickwick was excited and indignant. He beckoned to Mr Weller, and said in a stern voice, 'Take his skates off.'

'No; but really I had scarcely begun,' remonstrated Mr Winkle.

'Take his skates off,' repeated Mr Pickwick firmly.

The command was not to be resisted. Mr Winkle allowed Sam to obey it in silence.

'Lift him up,' said Mr Pickwick. Sam assisted him to rise.

Mr Pickwick retired a few paces apart from the bystanders; and, beckoning his friend to approach, fixed a searching look upon him, and uttered in a low, but distinct and emphatic tone, these remarkable words:

'You're a humbug sir.'

'A what?' said Mr Winkle, starting.

'A humbug, sir. I will speak plainer if you wish it. An imposter, sir.'

With those words, Mr Pickwick turned slowly on his heel, and rejoined his friends.

While Mr Pickwick was delivering himself of the sentiment just recorded, Mr Weller and the fat boy, having by their joint endeavours cut out a slide, were exercising themselves thereupon, in a very masterly and brilliant manner. Sam Weller, in particular, was displaying that beautiful feat of fancy-sliding which is currently denominated 'knocking at the cobbler's door', and which is achieved by skimming over the ice on one foot, and occasionally giving a postman's knock upon it with the other. It was a good long slide, and there was something in the motion which Mr Pickwick, who was very cold with standing still, could not help envying.

'It looks a nice warm exercise that, doesn't it' he inquired of Wardle, when that gentleman was thoroughly out of breath, by reason of the indefatigable manner in which he had converted his legs into a pair of compasses, and drawn complicated problems on the ice.

'Ah, it does indeed,' replied Wardle. 'Do you slide?'

'I used to do so, on the gutters, when I was a boy,' replied Mr Pickwick.

'Try it now,' said Wardle.

'Oh do please, Mr Pickwick!' cried all the ladies.

'I should be very happy to afford you any amusement,' replied Mr Pickwick, 'but I haven't done such a thing these thirty years.'

'Pooh! pooh! Nonsense!' said Wardle, dragging off his skates with the impetuosity which characterised all his proceedings. 'Here; I'll keep you company; come along!' And away went the good-tempered old fellow down the slide, with a rapidity which came very close upon Mr Weller, and beat the fat boy all to nothing.

Mr Pickwick paused, considered, pulled off his gloves and put them in his hat: took two or three short runs, baulked himself as often, and at last took another run, and went slowly and gravely down the slide, with his feet about a yard and a quarter apart, amidst the gratified shouts of all the spectators.

'Keep the pot a bilin', sir!' said Sam; and down went Wardle again, and then Mr Pickwick, and then Sam, and then Mr Winkle, and then Mr Bob Sawyer, and then the fat boy, and then Mr Snodgrass, following closely upon each other's heels, and running after each other with as much eagerness as if all their future prospects in life depended on their expedition.

It was the most intensely interesting thing, to observe the manner in which Mr Pickwick performed his share in the ceremony; to watch the torture of anxiety with which he viewed the person behind, gaining upon him at the imminent hazard of tripping him up; to see him gradually expend the painful force he had put on at first, and turn slowly round on the slide, with his face towards the point from which he had started; to contemplate the playful smile which mantled on his face when he had accomplished the distance, and the eagerness with which he turned round when he had done so, and ran after his predecessor: his black gaiters tripping pleasantly through the snow, and his eyes beaming cheerfulness and gladness through his spectacles. And when he was knocked down (which happened upon the average every third round), it was the most invigorating sight that can possibly be imagined to behold him gather up his hat, gloves, and handkerchief, with a glowing countenance, and resume his station in the rank, with an ardour and enthusiasm that nothing could abate.

The sport was at its height, the sliding was at the quickest, the laughter was at the loudest, when a sharp smart crack was heard. There was a quick rush towards the bank, a wild scream from the ladies, and a shout from Mr Tupman. A large mass of ice disappeared; the water bubbled up over it; Mr Pickwick's hat, gloves, and handkerchief were floating on the surface; and this was all of Mr Pickwick that anybody could see.

Dismay and anguish were depicted on every countenance, the males turned pale, and the females fainted, Mr Snodgrass and Mr. Winkle grasped each other by the hand, and gazed at the spot where their leader had gone down, with frenzied eagerness: while Mr Tupman, by way of rendering the promptest assistance, and at the same time conveying to any persons who might be within hearing, the clearest possible notion of the catastrophe, ran off across the country at his utmost speed, screaming 'Fire!' with all his might.

It was at this moment, when old Wardle and Sam Weller were approaching the hole with cautious steps, and Mr Benjamin Allen was holding a hurried consultation with Mr Bob Sawyer, on the advisability of bleeding the company generally, as an improving little bit of professional practice – it was at this very moment, that a face, head, and shoulders emerged from beneath the water, and disclosed the features and spectacles of Mr Pickwick.

'Keep yourself up for an instant – for only one instant!' bawled Mr Snodgrass.

'Yes, do; let me implore you – for my sake!' roared Mr Winkle deeply affected. The adjuration was rather unnecessary; the probability being that if Mr Pickwick had declined to keep himself up for anybody else's sake, it would have occurred to him that he might as well do so, for his own.

'Do you feel the bottom there, old fellow?' said Wardle.

'Yes, certainly,' replied Mr Pickwick, wringing the water from his head and face, gasping for breath. 'I fell upon my back. I couldn't get on my feet at first.'

The clay upon so much of Mr Pickwick's coat as was yet visable, bore testimony to the accuracy of this statement; and as the fears of the spectators were still further relieved by the fat boy's suddenly recollecting that the water was nowhere more than five feet deep, prodigies of valour were performed to get him out. After a vast quantity of splashing, and cracking, and struggling, Mr Pickwick was at length fairly extricated from his unpleasant position, and once more stood on dry land. . . .

'The Moon Shines Bright' – a Traditional Carol

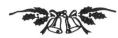

'The Moon Shines Bright' was a very popular carol in rural areas in the south of England in the nineteenth century. It was featured by groups of carol singers and was sometimes sung in association with mummer's plays. The obsession with the shortness of life is rather medieval and it may have originated as an Easter-tide Passion carol. Alternatively the austerity of the words may reflect a Puritan or Calvinistic overlay. The tune, however, is exceptionally beautiful, and some of the natural imagery and moving simplicity of the original words shines through the sombre religious message.

The famous folk-song collector Cecil Sharp collected this version of the carol from James Beale at Warehorne on 23 September 1908. Two of the verses are from other versions collected by Sharp and the carol is also found in collections such as Sandys' Christmas Carols *(1833).*

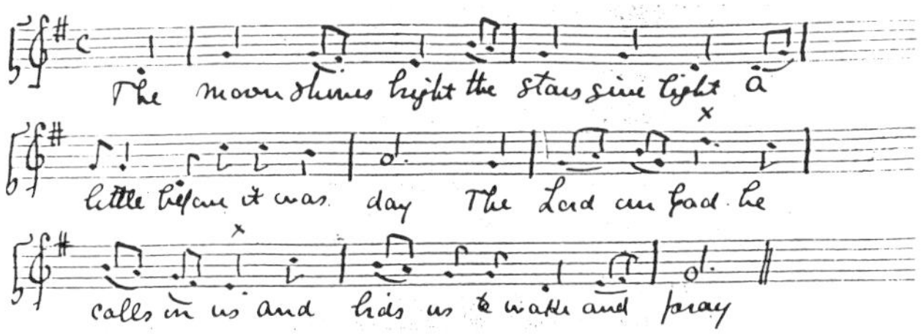

The moon shines bright the stars give light a
little before it was day The Lord our God he
calls on us and bids us to wake and pray

The moon shines bright, the stars give light
A little before it was day,
The Lord our God he calls on us
And bids us to wake and pray.

Awake, awake, good people all,
Awake and you shall hear
How our Lord our God died on the Cross
For us he lov-ed so dear.

In yonder garden green doth grow,
As green as any leek,
Our Lord our God he waters us
With his heavenly dew so sweet.

So teach your children well, dear man,
It's whilst that you are here.
It will be the better for your soul, dear man,
When you are gone from here.

To-day you might be alive, dear man,
And worth ten thousand pound;
Tomorrow you might be dead, dear man,
And your corpse lie underground.

The turf all at your head, dear man,
And another at your feet,
When your good deeds and your bad deeds
Before the Lord will meet.

The life of man is but a span,
And cut down in its flower.
We are here to-day and to-morrow are gone
We are all dead in an hour.

My song is done, I must be gone
I can stay no longer here,
God bless you all, both great and small,
And send you a happy New Year.

Murder in the Cathedral

Probably the most spectacular assassination in British history took place in Canterbury on the fourth day of Christmas in the year 1170 when Thomas à Becket, primate of all England, was murdered in his own cathedral.

Henry II, wishing to curtail the power of the Church in England, had appointed Thomas à Becket, his chancellor and friend, as Archbishop of Canterbury in the year 1162. Henry was disappointed to find that once in power, Thomas upheld the right of the Church to maintain its own laws and courts. The two quarrelled bitterly, after which Henry banished Thomas from England. Thomas went into exile in Europe, remaining there for six years. In 1170, Henry invited Thomas to return and the archbishop, amid great rejoicing, returned to Canterbury where 'crowds of poor, small and great, old and young, ran together, some throwing themselves in his way, others throwing down their garments for him to walk on.'

The feud between king and priest soon flared up again and on Christmas Day 1170 Becket preached an emotional Christmas sermon in his cathedral to an amazed congregation on the text 'On earth, peace to men of goodwill' at which he dramatically forecast his own death as a martyr. Thomas concluded the Christmas Day mass by excommunicating a number of his enemies – all friends and supporters of the king. This information was rapidly conveyed to Henry, at his court in France, who, legend has it, declared bitterly: 'Will no one rid me of this meddlesome priest?' Interpreting the king's words as a directive, four Norman knights, Richard le Breton, William de Tracy, Hugh Moreville and Reginald Fitzurse, crossed the Channel on 28 December in wintry seas, arriving in Canterbury on 29 December. They stormed into the archbishop's palace and, after an angry interview with Becket, withdrew in order to retrieve their swords. Becket was urged by his terrified attendants to seek sanctuary in the cathedral and as they hurried along the path through the cloister to the cathedral, they were closely followed by the four armed soldiers who pushed their way through a door now known as the Martyrdom Door. As Becket was ascending the steps which led to the choir the Normans surrounded him. Bitter words were spoken, and in their panic all the monks except one, Edward Grim, fled, while the knights attempted to drag Thomas from the sanctuary of the cathedral. Thomas fiercely resisted and stood with his back against a pillar while the soldiers raised their swords and struck. Edward Grim bravely attempted to ward off the first blow and was badly wounded. The second and subsequent blows found their mark. Becket fell dead, his body pierced and his head sliced through. As the murderers ran hurriedly from the cathedral the shaking witnesses noted the storm raging in the winter skies and lifting the body from the floor saw what they considered to be signs of Becket's great sanctity – a rough hair shirt worn next to the archbishop's flesh, and the body livid with fleas.

Christian Europe was shaken to its foundations. The Pope made his displeasure felt and Henry, obliged to appease the

Panel in Canterbury Cathedral, originally painted for the tomb of Henry IV, depicting the martyrdom of Becket

Church did public penance. Wearing only a rough woollen shirt and a pilgrim's cloak, the King of England in an attitude of humility, walked barefoot from the Church of St Dunstan, outside the city walls, to the great cathedral of Canterbury. In the crypt and before the tomb of his one-time friend and archbishop, Henry bent his back and was scourged by bishops and abbots. This ordeal was followed by a whipping as the eighty monks of Christ's Church came forward in turn and gave the king three strokes each.

Becket was canonized and his death day declared a saint's feast day. For the next three hundred years his shrine, jewel encrusted and of incalculable worth, was housed in a spacious chapel behind the great east altar in his cathedral and here his relics soon gained a reputation for working miracles. This shrine attracted visitors from all over Europe. It was the second most visited in Europe and brought enormous revenues to the cathedral.

The shrine itself was not the only visible relic of Becket. Pilgrims could visit the Transept of the Martyrdom where the point of Le Breton's sword was displayed. In the crypt Becket's skull, covered in silver, was venerated by pilgrims as was the saint's clothing, his hair shirt, belt and tunic. As a momento, pilgrims could buy in the catherdal tiny badges, lead ampulla containing 'Canterbury Water' which was reputed to be a drop of the martyr's blood mixed with water. The ampulla were usually stamped with the figure of St Thomas and the words, *Optimus egrorum medicus fit Thoma honorum.*

In 1320, one hundred and fifty years after the martyrdom, a jubilee to mark Becket's death was held in Canterbury and three more were held at fifty year intervals. At these jubilees plenary indulgences were issued to pilgrims (i.e., remission of all the temporal punishment due on sin in this world and the next). Among those who arrived to claim the jubilee indulgence in 1370 was the great English poet Geoffrey Chaucer and on his return he wrote *The Canterbury Tales*, the most famous tale of any pilgrimage made, and of how, at that period:

> . . . from every shire's end
> Of Engle-land to Canterbury they wend,
> The hold blissful martyr for to seek,
> That then hath holpen when that they were sick.

from

Bygone Kent – 'Christmas in Kent One Hundred Years Ago'

FLORENCE RICHARDSON

Judging by the reminiscences of my parents, Christmas one hundred years ago was a Church Festival and a time of family togetherness. Not a bit like the commercial bonanza that we call Christmas in 1983. Mind you, food and drink played an important part as well. For Christmas dinner, to most farm labourers and their families, was the highlight of their gastronomic year . . .

Some county clerics had 'The rich man in his castle, The poor man at his gate, God made them high or lowly, And ordered their estate' approach to their parishioners. But some Parsons would persuade the Scrooge-like farmers into a show of generosity at Christmas. Farmers would often have a pig killed at Christmas and give their men a large joint for the family dinner. An employee, fortunate enough to have a cockerel or rabbit already fattening up at home, would put his piece of

pork in his brine tub for meals in the lean cold days ahead. For pork was greatly prized, the fatter the better. Pork dripping was spread on bread for breakfast, tea, school lunches and labourers' meal breaks. The lard was used for pastry, and a little lard rubbed on to sore chapped hands and faces was a healing balm.

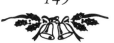

About a week before Christmas Day the Church choir would set out on their evening rounds. They would sing carols outside the wealthier houses and farms in the locality. Although my father's voice was more enthusiastic than tuneful he liked to go with the Fordwich Church choir carrying a lantern to show the way along the unlit roads and lanes. For, hopefully, some kind householders might invite the choir in for refreshments. That is if their boots were not too plastered with mud or snow.

Winters seemed to have been very severe with heavy snowfalls a century ago. As a child I used to love to hear my parents' stories about the Blizzard of 1881. My father and two of his brothers were at Sturry School when the snow started to fall. Fortunately, a kindly, weatherwise farmer noticed the way the snow was piling up into deep drifts. He sent two of his men in a farm wagon to take the school children to their homes. It was a slow, cold journey sitting in straw and covered with sacks, but everyone got delivered safely to his home.

At that time my mother's family were living at Hoath, a village about five miles north of Canterbury. She and her sisters were sent home from school early in the day, and did not go out again for six weeks. Her father was in charge of the farm horses at Ford Manor, a farm situated between two hills. Their home was a cottage at the top of one of the hills. Grandfather used to walk on top of the hedge to guide himself through the deep snow down to the farm stables. Here he performed a prodigious digging effort to tunnel his way through to feed and water the horses. His cottage well was frozen up, so on the return journey he took back water from the farm's indoor pump in two buckets hanging from a shoulder yoke. Sometimes Grandfather took a swede home in his pocket for his wife to boil and mash with potatoes. Fortunately, like most country people, they kept a sack of potatoes indoors through the winter as well as the saltpork bin.

Indoor, Christmas decorations were a few sprigs of holly and sprays of ivy hung round the pictures. Most families would make a small wreath of greenery to place on the grave of a baby brother or sister as they went to Church on Christmas Day. My mother used to recall how her mother, every year, would bring out a small doll dressed in white to adorn the mantlepiece. Although they were not allowed to touch the doll, they loved looking up at it in the firelight. To them it represented the Christ Child and was their symbol of Christmas.

How splendid those village Churches must have looked, with the altar cross, lighted candles, crib and choir, to those children from small, overcrowded homes. They would gaze in awe as they joined in singing the Christmas hymns they would have learned at Day School. (And of course they were used to sitting on the benches while the Upper Crust sat in the box pews wrapped in rugs, as they did at Fordwich village church!)

Children with older brothers and sisters might be lucky enough to get a small Christmas gift. As my mother was one of the eldest in the family she never expected a present. She received her first gift when she went into service. An apron! My father had older sisters, who gave their mother a shawl, which doubled as a bed cover. Their younger brothers were given an orange each and perhaps a pencil or crayon, which would be greatly prized. (In those days grocers bought by bulk and packaged the goods themselves. They used thick white paper as wrappers which the cottage children used as writing or drawing paper.)

The fruitiness of the Christmas pudding often depended on how well the hop picking money had lasted. But their basic ingredients of flour, beef suet and black treacle made a filling and nutritious pudding, even if the raisins and currants were a bit scarce.

Teenage boys and girls, who lived in as farmhouse and farm workers, were nearly always treated as family at Christmas and given some good meals by the farmer's wife. These good ladies were often much softer hearted than their spouses.

In these days of mains and Calor Gas, pre-set electric and microwave ovens, it is difficult to visualise the cooking of a Christmas dinner, in a cottage during the early 1880s, for about eight people. Small wood faggots would have been used to heat up the interior of the bread oven. When the loaves had been baked, the brick oven would still retain enough heat to roast a joint of pork or a cockerel. The vegetables would be cooked in a pot hanging from a hook over the open fire, while the Christmas pudding would bubble gently in an iron saucepan standing on a trivet that was fixed on the top bar of the open fire. This fire had to be constantly stoked with chopped wood as it warmed the room and aired washing as well as keeping the pots boiling. After the family had enjoyed their best meal of the year, Grandfather would have a short nap while Grandmother did the washing up. The older children would bring in wood to dry for use the next day, fill up buckets with water from the outside well or pump and check that there were candles ready for evening use. Then the family would put on their outdoor clothes, bank up the fire and set off to visit older relations. That is, those who lived within walking distance (about three miles each way).

When their families worked away from home, the parents were often sent a likeness (photograph) with the Christmas letters. This gave visitors a chance to see the latest photos and catch up on the family news. Older relatives, too were often very good at making home-made wine. A sample of their particular brew (watered down for the children) and a piece of cake was a great treat. All feeling a little tipsy, they would walk home under the stars. Sometimes they met up with neighbours, also out on a mission of goodwill and family togetherness.

On their return the family would toast chestnuts and tell scary ghost stores. But after a cup of cocoa the children were sent to bed tired out after carols in Church, plenty to eat and convivial family visits. Their parents soon followed, thankful for such a happy Christmas Day. Tomorrow would be back to work as usual.

A Christmas Poacher

TONBRIDGE FREE PRESS

2 JANUARY 1942

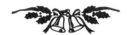

Traditionally, Christmas fare was supplemented among the poorer classes in the rural areas by discreet poaching. It is interesting to note from this Tonbridge newspaper extract that it was still being done as recently as 1942, though the shortage of food during wartime may, of course, have been a factor.

The SEASON'S Compliments.

Poacher Fined

John C— of 6, Colts Hill Cottages, Capel, was summoned at Tonbridge Police Court on Tuesday last week by Walter T— of W— Farm, Capel, for trespassing on his property in search of conies.

Mr T—, in evidence said while out with his gun on his estate, he found defendant over a rabbit hole. When ordered off, defendant refused to go until he had retrieved his ferret. Witness said he would take a summons out against the defendant, and left him near the rabbit hole.

Corroborative evidence was given by an estate employee.

Defendant, who did not apear in court, wrote pleading guilty and said he thought he was doing good by helping to exterminate rabbits, which were a nuisance in that part of the country. He added that he wanted a meal for his wife and children.

Defendant, described as a married man with six children, was fined 5s.

Highwaymen in Eighteenth-Century Kent

MAIDSTONE JOURNAL
23 JANUARY 1787

Despite all the romantic literature concerning them, the 'gentlemen of the road' in the seventeenth and eighteenth centuries were a real and dangerous threat to society. Basically thieves, they often combined their nocturnal robberies with cattle-stealing and smuggling. Wentworth, when he is committed to Newgate in this extract, had every right to be 'affected with his unhappy situation', for numbers of his fellow highwaymen had taken their last journey from this prison to the gallows at Tyburn for a like offence.

On Monday two highwaymen who committed many robberies on Blackheath and the Kentish roads during the course of last-week, were examined at the public office in Bow-Street. Several gentlemen attended who have recently been robbed, when sufficient proof of their guilt appearing, they were ordered for examination before Sir S. Wright and Mr Justice Addington on Friday last, concerning the robbery of Alderman

Curtis, and another gentleman – No other evidence appearing to incriminate them, Manning was discharged; but without of sensible, feeling and furious admonition from Sir Sampson Wright, relative to his future conduct. – Wentworth was committed to Newgate for trial, at our next assizes. – It is said he is of good family, and was bred a surgeon, since which he has served as an officer in one of the provincial Corps in Ireland. – He appeared very much affected with his unhappy situation; into which he has undoubtedly been drawn by a deliberately designing villain, who has thus far escaped the hands of justice.

Acknowledgements

All unattributed items are by Geoff and Fran Doel.

Extracts from *Shipwrecks of the Goodwin Sands* by Richard Larn (David and Charles) by kind permission of the publishers. The articles 'A Christmas Mystery'; 'Fattening the Chickens', 'Royal Christmases at Eltham' and 'Christmas in Kent One Hundred Years Ago', were first printed in the monthly publication *Bygone Kent* and are reproduced by kind permission of the owner, Mr Mackay Miller, editor, Miss Pat O'Driscoll and the authors. The extract from *Hughes the Wer-wolf* is reproduced by kind permission of Alan Castle from his 1989 edition published by Folk Spots. The accounts of 'Christmas at Leeds Castle' were kindly researched for the book by Mrs Joanna Oswin, Marketing Manager, Mr David Clegget, Official Historian to Leeds Castle Foundation and Mr John Money who was agent to Lady Baillie from 1926 to 1975. The Kent version of 'The Seven Joys of Mary' was kindly supplied by Simon Evans. Joris Field's article on 'Santa Specials' was first published in *Folk In Kent* in April 1990 and is reproduced by kind permission of the editor, Jack Hamilton. Derek Smith, Marketing Manager of the Romney, Hythe and Dymchurch Light Railway Company sent the photograph and information used in the introduction. Frank Atkinson, Librarian at St Paul's Cathedral, directed our attention to William Beatty's *Narrative of the Death of Lord Nelson* and kindly allowed us to examine the official funeral programme. Iain MacKenzie of the Enquiry Services at the National Maritime Museum, Greenwich provided information on Lord Nelson's lying in state. The article 'A Small Parcel' by Richard Church is taken from his book *A Window on a Hill* and is reproduced by kind permission of his estate. Brian Holloway, landlord of the Bell and Jorrocks Inn, Frittenden kindly supplied information and a drawing of the Frittenden Band. David Cousins, Canterbury reference librarian kindly supplied information on *The Plum Pottage Riots*. The article 'Christmas Presents' is an extract from the chapter 'Christmas Day' in Frank Kendon's book *The Small Years*. This is used by kind permission of Cambridge University Press and Frank Kendon's estate. The Twelfth Cake recipe (collected by Catherine Rothwell) is reproduced by kind permission of Hendon Publishing Co. Ltd. from their book *Old Kent Recipes*. Peter Battrick of the National Trust kindly supplied information on Christmases at Chartwell. Malcolm Taylor, librarian of the English Folk Dance and Song Society kindly assisted us with Cecil Sharp's collected versions of 'The Moon Shines Bright'. 'A Christmas Poacher' was first published in the *Tonbridge Free Press* and is reproduced by kind permission of *The Kent Messenger*. Alan Austen and Les Waghorn kindly provided information on Christmas songs in Kent and Alan suggested the use of the 'Hengist's Daughter' story.

Picture Credits

The Tunnicliffe Trustees 48; Beverley Smith, Marketing Services, Shepway District Council 6; Archie Turnbull 11, 83, 118; Glenn Miller 15; Pat Dixon 17; Norman Rout 16; The Victorian Greeting Cards on pp. 20, 51, 80, 98, 106, 149, 150, 153, 154, 155 can be obtained from East Anglian Cards, Curtons House, Walpole St Peter, Wisbech, Cambs or from most museums and galleries; C.M. Dalton, Maritime and Local History Museum, Deal 33; Kent Arts and Libraries Department 34 top and bottom, 103; Carson Ritchie 37, 39, 42, 43, 44; Fran Doel 52, 123; Annis Cumfrey 56, 58; The Friars Aylesford 62; Percy Maylam 66, 67; Pete Castle, folksinger and artist, c/o A. Castle 15 Repton Manor Road, Ashford, Kent 72; Leeds Castle 78; R.H. & D. Light Railway 85; Greenwich Maritime Museum 88, 89; Hever Castle 92, 132 (top); Alan Sutton 1, 96, 97; Geoff Doel, 126, 132 (bottom); Jim Landergan 110; Mary Digby 129; Canterbury Cathedral Archives 146; Brian Holloway 100. We should particularly like to thank Norman Rout for his assistance and advice in processing several of the photographs and Archie Turnbull for providing us with a number of photographs and photographic advice. Mr Turnbull's photographs of stained glass at St Mary the Virgin, Speldhurst and All Saints, Maidstone are included with the kind permission of the vicars.